HYDROSTATIC POWER TRANSMISSION

D1328227

HYDROSTATIC POWER TRANSMISSION

By

JEAN U. THOMA

Dr.Sc., phys. dipl. EPF, A.M.I.Mar.E.

Consultant for hydrostatic
transmissions and controls

Published by
Trade and Technical Press, Limited, Morden, Surrey, England

Published simultaneously in German under the title "Hydrostatische Geteriebe frier Leistungsuebertragung" by Carl Hanser, Verlag, Munich.

This edition made and printed in the Republic of Ireland by Hely Thom Limited, Dublin

PREFACE

THE object of this book is to assist in the practice of hydrostatic transmission and its application. It results from the experience of the author as a consultant for hydrostatic transmission and control systems, and describes the problems met most frequently in industry.

After an introduction, properties of hydrostatic units are given, followed by chapter 2 on variable power transmission in general. Hydrostatic transmissions as such are discussed in chapter 3, control of transmissions in chapter 4, properties of combined hydrostatic and mechanical elements, including split power drives, in chapter 5, while the last chapter treats some application problems. The table of contents will give a more precise idea of the scope and coverage of this book.

The bibliography at the end of the book provides a selection of books on hydraulics and control engineering, which the author has found useful in the practice of hydrostatic transmission.

Although the author is not a university teacher many of his consulting visits have some of the atmosphere of a teaching session and the presentation of this text is governed by the author's experience and his desire to make the subject matter, ideas and concepts most easily understandable.

Throughout the treatment the point of view of feed back control engineering is always considered without making feed back control theory a prerequisite for understanding the main text, but a little more advanced treatment of some feed back questions is contained in the appendix. This is due to the fact that a variable speed transmission has to be controlled either manually or better, automatically, which almost always necessitates feed back control. Indeed the ultimate goal, namely, the satisfaction of the user, depends on the correct operation of the whole system including controls, where the hydrostatic transmission is just one link—usually the one carrying the highest power. For readers wishing to experience the appeal and beauty of feed back control theory, the text B6 of the bibliography is recommended as an introduction.

Some emphasis is given to experiments with hydrostatic units and hydrostatic transmission, which might be possible in industry. Since a variable hydrostatic transmission forms a very versatile piece of machinery, it allows many experiments to be made easily, and is a source not only of important information, but also of professional satisfaction to the engineer.

JEAN U. THOMA

Zug, Switzerland
Spring 1964

ACKNOWLEDGMENTS

THE author is indebted above all to his father, Hans W. Thoma, Prof. emeritus, Dr. Ing, who for the last forty years has been the master of scientific treatment of all phases of hydrostatic transmissions (and other branches of engineering). From him, the author had an early and uninterrupted instruction and teaching in this field and many of the new concepts and experiments of this book were originally devised by him.

Furthermore, the following firms with whom the author enjoys close relationship as a consultant, have indirectly contributed to this book, by making apparent the necessity, form and scope of a desirable treatment of hydrostatic transmission:

George Angus and Co. Ltd.,	Newcastle upon Tyne,	England
Institut Battelle,	Geneva,	Switzerland
Cattermole Hydraulics Ltd.,	Redditch,	England
C. Galdabini S.p.A.	Gallarate,	Italy
Officine Galileo,	Florence,	Italy
Hydromatik G.m.b.H.,	Ulm,	Germany
Litmat S.n.C.,	Turin	Italy

The figures 1.1–6 and 3.4–3 have been supplied by Cattermole, the figures I–2, I–3, I–4 and 4.2–4 by Galdabini, and are hereby gratefully acknowledged.

The Author's wife has participated in this work by typing the whole of the English and German editions of this book.

CONTENTS

NOTATION

Every effort has been made to use a consistent notation. To this end indices have been used, which are, as far as possible, selfexplanatory. The index 1 refers to primary, index 2 to secondary, index 0 to flow, pressure etc. with maximum displacement and ignoring losses.

In some of the following the correct physical dimension has been added in square brackets.

k = spring constant [kgf/sec]

n = rotative speed [1/sec]

n_1 = speed of primary

n_2 = speed of secondary

n_r = reference speed

n_{in}, n_u = input and output speed of superposition gearbox

n_u = output or load speed if different from n_2

$n_{2, a}, n_{2b}$ = speed of two secondaries in parallel

n_{2dir} = highest secondary speed with maximum torque

n_{1max} = highest input or engine speed

n_{2max} = highest secondary speed possible

n_{umax} = Highest load speed

n_{2pa}, n_{2pb} = highest secondary speed with full primary displacement in 2 choices, a and b of secondary speed range.

p = pressure [kgf/cm^2]

p_a, p_b = Pressure in main conduits a and b

p_r = reference pressure

$p_{ac} = p_a - P_c$ = acting pressure

p_{dir} = highest pressure with full primary displacement

q = displacement of hydrostatic unit [cm^3]

q_0 = Maximum displacement with $\alpha = 1$

q_1 = primary displacement

q_2 = secondary displacement

v = fluid velocity

x = position

x_p = Piston position

x_v = valve position

z = number of cylinders

B = bulk modulus [kgf/cm^2]

C = Dimensionless coefficient [1]

C_c = compressibility loss coefficient

C_f = dry friction loss coefficient

C_h = hydrodynamic loss coefficient

C_s = leakage coefficient

C_v = viscous friction coefficient

$I = \rho q_0{}^{5/3}$ = Constant factor dependant on hydro-dynamical losses [kgf Sec²cm]

J = moment of inertia [kgf Sec² cm]

L = length [cm]

M = turning moment or torque [kgf cm]

M_o = loss free torque with full displacement

M_1 = primary torque

M_2 = secondary torque

M_e = effective torque

M_f = dry friction torque

M_h = Hydrodynamical loss torque

$M_i = aM_o$ = ideal torque

M_l = loss torque in general

M_s = slip torque

M_v = viscous friction torque

M_u = load or output torque if different from M_2

M_r = reference torque

M_{fr}, M_{hr}, M_{vr} = reference loss torques defined by equation 12–16

M_{in} = input torque of superposition gearbox in see 52

M_{2a}, M_{2b} = torques of secondaries in parallel

M_{1l}, M_{2l} = primary and secondary loss torques

M_{2r} = reference secondary torque for propeller drives

M_{2dir} = highest secondary torque in direct ratio

M_{1max} = highest input torque

M_{2max} = highest possible secondary torque

M_{umax} = highest load torque

M_{pm} = torque of prime mover

M_{2bs} = secondary torque in fixed shaft experiment

M_{lop}, M_{1bp} = loss torque in the open and blocked port experiment

M_{los}, M_{1bs} = loss torques in the open and blocked port experiment

P = Power [kgf cm/Sec]

P_e = effective power

P_i = input power

P_l = loss power

P_r = reference power

P_{ap} = apparent power

P_{me} = effective mechanical power

P_{he} = effective hydraulic power

P_{lop}, P_{1bp} = lost power in open and blocked port experiment

P_{los}, P_{lbs} = lost power in open and blocked shaft experiment

Q = Flow rate [cm³/Sec]

Q_o = loss-free flow with maximum displacement

Q_a, Q_b = flow in two secondaries, a and b, in parallel

Q_c = compressibility flow

Q_e = effective flow

$Q_i = \alpha Q_o$ = ideal flow

Q_s = leakage or slip flow

Q_v = valve flow

Q_r = reference flow

Q_{sr} = reference slip flow

Q_{iz} = ideal delivery flow of one cylinder

Q_{max}, Q_{min} = maximum and minimum flow depending on shaft position in Sec. 13 b

S = Section or Area [cm²]

V = Volume [cm³]

V^1 = switching volume

V_o = displacement or swept volume of one cylinder

ΔV = change of volume under pressure

V_{re} = residual volume in cylinder at idc.

α = displacement setting, variable between 0 and 1 in one-way pumps, and between -1 and $+1$ in reversing hydrostatic units [1]

α_1 = primary displacement setting

α_2 = secondary displacements setting

α_s = slip displacement setting, defined by equa. 12–2

γ = torque multiplication [1]

γ_s = torque multiplication at stall

δ = clearance [cm]

η = efficiency [1]

μ = viscosity [kgf Sec/cm²]

π = 3.14159

ρ = mass density of fluid [kgt Sec²/cm⁴]

ρ_1, ρ_2, ρ_i = gear ratios of power split transmission

ωt = rotative position of drive shaft

INTRODUCTION

THIS book deals with the quantitative aspects of hydrostatic transmissions for producing a controlled and variable speed for all drive requirements in engineering. In order to place the main discussions on a definite basis, in this introduction the elementary aspects of design and operation of a hydrostatic transmission will be summarized.

In a hydrostatic transmission the mechanical energy of the input drive shaft is converted into pressure energy in the nearly incompressible working fluid and then reconverted into mechanical energy at the output shaft. Essentially, therefore, a hydrostatic transmission consists of a pump driven by an input shaft supplying fluid to a motor driving the output shaft, as shown in the hydraulic circuit in fig. I–1. It is usual to denote as the primary hydrostatic unit the unit coupled to the input shaft and secondary hydrostatic unit the unit coupled to the output shaft, in preference to the expressions "pump" and "motor".

In the preferred arrangement shown on fig. I–1, the primary is of variable displacement, as indicated by the arrow. Therefore the

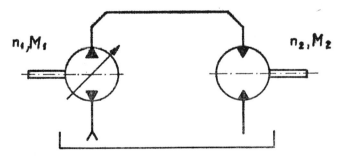

I–1 Simple hydrostatic transmission with open circuit and primary control

flow produced with a given input speed is variable depending on the selected displacement. It is fed into a constant displacement secondary which drives the output shaft with a speed corresponding to the flow. Disregarding leakage losses, the speed ratio given by the ratio of the effective displacements is:

$$\frac{n_2}{n_1} = \frac{q_1}{q_2} = a \text{ with } q_1 = a\, q_0, \text{ and } q_2 = q_0 \qquad \cdot\cdot \qquad (1)$$

n_1, n_2 = input, output shaft speed

q_1, q_2 = effective displacement of primary, secondary

The ratio of the output to the input torque in a lossless transmission is given by the reciprocal of the speed ratio in accordance with the principle of conservation of energy:

$$\frac{M_2}{M_1} = \frac{q_2}{q_1} = \frac{1}{a} \qquad \cdot\cdot \qquad (2)$$

M_1, M_2 = torques of input, output shaft

The above formulas are frequently used for initial determination of a hydrostatic transmission for a given application. It should also be noted that the product of speed and torque in each shaft is proportional to the power carried therein, with a constant of proportionality depending on the units. The modifications of equations (1) and (2) necessary to take into account the various losses are given in section 3.3.

A characteristic of hydrostatic transmission as opposed to hydrodynamic or hydrokinetic transmission is that the energy is carried by the static energy content of the fluid flow and not by the kinetic energy associated with fluid velocity. This means that the static pressure is much higher than the dynamic pressure corresponding to the highest fluid velocities.

For high power density and reasonable compactness of transmission, it is necessary to select comparatively high pressures. Numerical values of course depend on the application, but in 1964 a continuous pressure of 150 kgf/cm^2 (2 150 psi) and an overload pressure of 330 kgf/cm^2 (4 700 psi) seems standard. The fluid velocities in the pipes and components should not exceed 10 m/sec (33 ft/sec) corresponding to a dynamic pressure of 0.5 kgf/cm^2 (7 psi) so that there is a definite preponderance of static pressure over dynamic pressure.

The use of these very high pressures depends on the availability of hydrostatic variable and fixed displacement units capable of withstanding the corresponding loads during the required life. As an example, in figures I–2 and I–3 are shown a variable and fixed displacement unit designed by the author.

I-2 Variable displacement hydrostatic unit, of the bent axis type, suitable for transmission applications

I-3 Fixed displacement hydrostatic unit of bent axis type

I–4 Hydrostatic machine tool transmission, 35 HP input power

For compact transmissions it is very desirable to choose the shaft speeds as high as is possible without danger of the sliding surfaces seizing. This again depends on the life required, and for continuous duty industrial drive speeds are generally limited to 1 500 or 1 800 rpm, for direct coupling to A.C. induction motors up to about 50 H.P. For larger power ratings, lower speeds are preferred for industrial use. In applications requiring the highest possible compactness including vehicle drives, higher speeds (about 3 000 rpm max.), are usual in order to allow direct coupling to internal combustion engines. For direct coupling to normal motor car engines running around 5 000 rpm some more development work will be required.

In many applications it is an advantage to separate primary and secondary units and to connect them by pipes. An example of such a transmission for machine tool drive transmitting 35 HP at 1 500 rpm is shown in fig. I–4. For testing purposes this transmission is loaded with a flywheel, as will be further described in detail in section 3.4.

Hydrostatic transmission uses the pressure energy of the fluid, which should therefore be as nearly incompressible as possible. Furthermore it must have good lubricating properties, in order that it may also be used to lubricate the very highly loaded sliding surfaces in the hydrostatic units. Also it should have sufficient viscosity to reduce leakage through small clearances to acceptable values and this viscosity should not vary too much with temperature. Therefore normal lubricating machine oil has been used for a long time and it is only now being superseded by the special hydraulic oils supplied by the Oil Industry. Since even a small amount of air inclusion in the oil increases the compressibility appreciably, the design of the transmission should aim to avoid such air inclusion, mainly by preventing contact of turbulent oil with the atmosphere.

The advantage of hydrostatic transmission is that by a simple resetting of the displacement of the primary the output speed can be continuously selected. Output speed can be maintained very nearly independent of the torque required on the output shaft, if the input speed is held constant. Reversing output rotation, picking loads up from rest, and dynamic braking with feed back of the energy to the input shaft are also possible.

The limitations of hydrostatic transmissions derive from the fact that they involve the double conversion from a rotative mechanical energy to fluid pressure energy and back to mechanical energy. Therefore some bulk, cost and loss of efficiency results, although this can be reduced by modern designs and production methods.

It is the purpose of the following treatment of hydrostatic transmissions to discuss in detail the behaviour and testing of the different components, namely the variable and fixed displacement units that make up a hydrostatic transmission, and to give information how they can be combined to the best advantage into an hydrostatic transmission suitable for each application.

Oil hydraulic presses are a modified form of hydrostatic transmission where a very large force has to be produced over a limited stroke by a ram. Although many of the considerations in this book are applicable to hydraulic presses, they have many special problems and advantages of their own which lie outside the scope of the present book, but the author hopes to treat them fully on a later occasion.

CHAPTER 1

GENERATION OF HYDROSTATIC POWER

1.1 Hydrostatic Units

a) *Principles*

Hydrostatic transmission depends on the conversion of mechanical energy into a controlled flow of high pressure fluid. The apparatus effecting this conversion is properly called a hydrostatic unit, though the looser terms of oil pump or motor are some times used. Before proceeding to a classification of practical hydrostatic units a few fundamental remarks on their operation may be appropriate.

Hydrostatic units are energy converters of the displacement type. For a pumping unit this means, that a certain volume, usually a cylinder, filled with intake oil, is disconnected from an intake port and connected to a delivery port. Then the volume decreases, by inward travel of the piston, and the fluid is delivered against the pressure in the delivery port. When the displacement volume has reached its minimum, i.e. at inner dead centre of the piston travel, it is sealed from the delivery port and connected again to the intake port. The displacement volume increases to its former value, as the piston is travelling outward, drawing fluid from the intake port and thereby completing the cycle. In a motoring unit, the same cycle is run through in reverse.

It is necessary that the connections between the displacement volume and the intake or delivery ports are established at the correct moment by suitable valving. In a unit acting as pump only, this can be done simply by fitting non-return valves into the inlet and delivery port as it is known and usual in pump design. These valves are then fluid pressure operated and establish the required connection at the correct moment.

In unit working as a hydraulic motor, the valving cannot be done by fluid pressure, but must be done by mechanical means. It may take the form of eccentric driven seating or sliding valves, but more generally they are formed by slots milled in different surfaces brought alternatively into register by relative sliding movement.

A unit with a mechanically driven valving mechanism will be referred to as having a positive distribution. In the following, a

2

"hydrostatic transmission unit" will always be understood to be a displacement unit with positive distribution, because only such units are also workable as a motor. For completeness it should be mentioned, that there exist many satisfactory hydraulic pumps with fluid pressure actuated distribution, although at higher rotative speeds the inertia effects of the moving parts of the non-return valves cause incorrect timing.

Hydrostatic units can transform mechanical rotative energy into fluid pressure energy or hydrostatic power, and vice versa. Their most important parameter is the swept volume or the amount of fluid delivered against no pressure for one shaft revolution. Neglecting for the moment leakage and other inevitable losses, the shaft speed and torque are connected with the fluid flow, pressure and swept volume by the following:

$$Q = nq = naq_0 \qquad\qquad .. \qquad (1.1\text{--}1)$$

Q = flow rate

n = shaft speed

q = swept volume

a = displacement setting

q_0 = maximum displacement

$$p = \frac{2\pi M}{q} = \frac{2\pi M}{aq_0} \qquad\qquad .. \qquad (1.1\text{--}2)$$

p = pressure

M = torque (turning moment)

The power converted is proportional to flow multiplied by pressure and to shaft speed multiplied by torque:

$$P = Q\,p = 2\pi Mn \qquad\qquad .. \qquad (1.1\text{--}3)$$

P = power

It should be noted that these relations are physical formulae valid for any set of consistent units, but modified formulae valid with practical units are contained in table 1.1–1.

The operation of hydrostatic units can also be described by visualizing a unit coupled to a shaft with constant torque and a system with constant pressure. If the torque is greater than the corresponding pressure given by formulae 1.1–2 the unit will start pumping, but

Table 1.1-1

Fundamental equations of hydrostatic units in practical units :

$$Q = \frac{1}{277}\, nq = \frac{1}{277}\, anq_0$$

$$p = 75\,\frac{M}{q} = 75\,\frac{M}{aq_0}$$

$$P = \frac{1}{1420}\, Q.p = \frac{1}{525}\, Mn$$

$$Q = \text{Imp. g. pm}$$
$$q = \text{in}^3$$
$$p = \text{psi}$$
$$M = \text{lb ft}$$
$$P = \text{H.P.}$$
$$n = \text{rpm}$$

if the pressure is greater, the unit will start motoring by rotating in the reverse sense. Naturally there is a dead band with no rotation, due to friction in the unit, but with modern designs this is quite small.

Since it is the main object of hydrostatic transmission to obtain a controlled variable output speed from constant input speed, it is necessary to be able to vary the swept volume. Generally the design of hydrostatic units is governed by this necessity together with a very high force and power density. Many schemes have been proposed in the past for this purpose, and it is intended only to describe here a few of the more practical ones. For an exhaustive review and treatment of possible variable displacement mechanisms the reader is referred to the excellent book by R. Hadeckel. (Bibliography 9).

An example of a successful variable hydrostatic unit is derived from the vane pump. The swept volume is controlled by varying the eccentricity between rotor and the stator ring and some designs incorporate a constant pressure device, which reduces the output of the pump as a set pressure is reached. Due to large unbalanced fluid forces this design is limited to comparatively low pressures, but it is very successful within its range.

For higher pressures most hydrostatic units are of piston and cylinder type, because it is comparatively easy to produce cylinders and pistons to the accuracy required for acceptable leakage losses. The swept volume is varied by altering the stroke of the pistons. This has the effect that the dead centres of piston travel change their position with variation of displacement.

In order to obtain a variable stroke from the normal crank mechanism, it is possible to interpose between crank shaft and piston a rocking member, similar to the drive of the steam valve in steam locomotives. This mechanism is shown schematically in fig. 1.1–1 on a pump fitted with non-return valves. It would be possible to equip this mechanism with positive distribution by actuating the valves through eccentrics from the crank shaft. The design shown in fig. 1.1–1 can be made to pump non-lubricating fluids and is there-fore suitable as a metering pump for chemicals. In order to reduce the delivery fluctuations, it is possible to drive several pistons from one crank shaft. This is treated in detail in section 1.3–6.

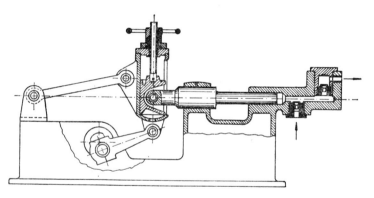

1.1–1 Example of variable displacement pump with crankshaft and rocker

b) *Compact multicylinder hydrostatic units*

For variable displacement hydrostatic units it is the general practice to arrange a plurality of cylinders with pistons in one cylinder block, normally rotating, and to provide suitable means for varying the piston stroke and for fluid distribution.

A widely used mechanism of this class is the radial piston pump, represented in fig. 1.1–2. Here the pistons are arranged radially in a rotating cylinder block and driven with variable stroke by an outer ring rotating with controlled eccentricity in respect to the cylinder block. The distribution of fluid is usually done by a pintle valve consisting of a non-rotating pintle with milled admission and delivery ports, lapped into a corresponding bore in the cylinder block in which are the cylinder ports. This design is suitable for high pressures, but the rotative speed tends to be limited by the size of the flow passages that can be accommodated in the pintle, and

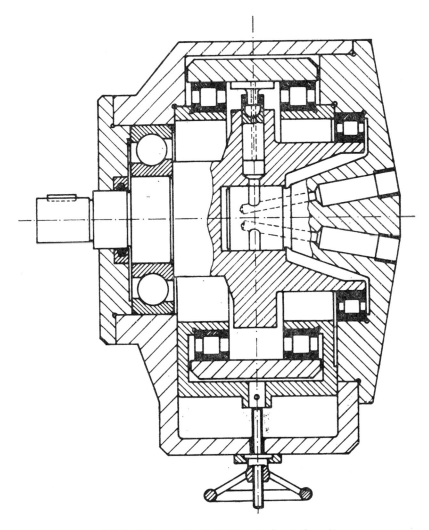

1.1–2 Scheme of radial piston hydrostatic unit

also by the centrifugal effects of the large diameter rotor. Hydrostatic units of this general type are produced by many manufacturers throughout the world.

Another practical class of variable displacement hydrostatic unit is the axial piston type, where a number of cylinders are arranged in a cylinder block parallel to its axis of revolution. While the distribution of the fluid is usually effected by the valve faces of the rotating cylinder block and the stationary distributor with milled admission and delivery ports, several methods are used to provide a variable stroke for the pistons.

One method of driving the pistons is to link them through connecting rods to a rotating disc fixed obliquely or tilted with respect to the shaft around an axis fixed in space. This design is shown schematically in fig. 1.1–3. It has been used for many years in hydrostatic transmissions, but the universal joint needed to transmit the torque between the driving disc and the shaft limits the allowable pressure.

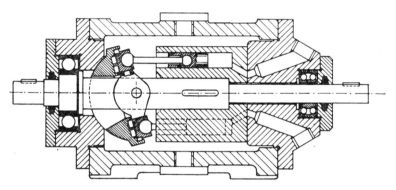

1.1–3 Scheme of axial piston hydrostatic unit with fully loaded universal joint

Another method of driving the piston consists of a non-rotating driving disc arranged so that its angle of tilt in the pump casing can be varied (fig. 1.1–4.) The pistons and connecting rods are combined and the driving disc thrust is taken through spherically seated slippers. Due to the piston force on the inclined disc a side force is created, which is transmitted back by the rigid piston as cantilever loading on the cylinder block. This produces the useful torque in the cylinder block and is from there transmitted by a coupling to the drive shaft.

The rigid piston units described here have the advantage of mechanically simple construction and have therefore been very

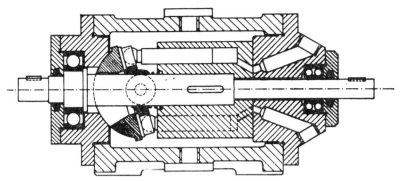

1.1–4 Scheme of piston hydraulic unit of the rigid piston type

popular in recent years. Its disadvantages are the cantilever side loads on the cylinder walls and the slippers sliding with high speed circumferentially on the inclined disc.

Another widely used design of variable hydrostatic unit employs a rotating drive disc (usually called a **drive** flange) integral with the drive shaft. In order to produce piston motion the entire head of the pump with cylinder block, distributor etc, is tilted around a transverse axis as shown schematically in fig. 1.1–5. Thus the universal joint between cylinder block and drive flange has only to provide proper synchronization or angular alignment between

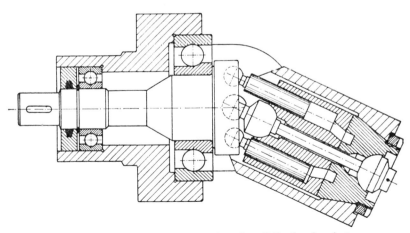

1.1–5 Scheme of piston hydraulic units of the bend axis type

cylinder block and drive flange and is therefore relieved from the main torque. Naturally the drive shaft must be properly supported to transmit its radial and axial loads to the casing, which is done in small hydrostatic units by roller bearings and in large units by hydrostatic plain bearings. In order to transmit the oil from the tilting distributor face, the trunnions have to be hollow. A perspective drawing of such a hydrostatic unit of recent design is given in fig. 1.1–6, while photographs of actual units of this design were reproduced in figs. I–2 and I–3. (p. 15)

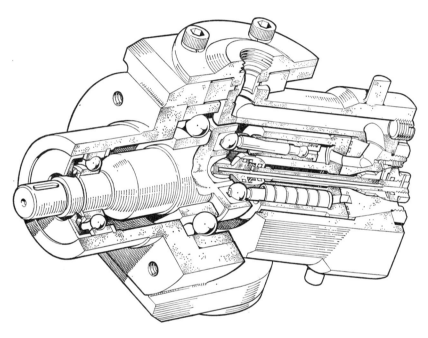

1.1–6 Perspective drawing a recent variable displacement axial piston hydraulic unit.

The advantage of the "bent axis" hydrostatic units is in the direct and favourable load distribution over all members according to their capability. This results in very low leakage and dry friction losses. A disadvantage is the somewhat larger bulk because of the space required to swing the tilting head round, and of the impossibility of having the drive shaft projecting at both ends of the casing. Generally the author has always preferred this type, after extensive study of the different possibilities, for variable displacement hydrostatic transmission units suitable for high speeds.

1.2 A) Losses in hydrostatic units

The purpose of a hydrostatic transmission is to produce with acceptable efficiency an output speed and torque, variable through a range of values in accordance with the control signals and load characteristics which are treated in detail in chapter 2. It is therefore necessary to use hydrostatic units, which are efficient over the whole range of operating variables—speed, pressure and displacement setting—and not only at an optimum point. In order to place the study of hydrostatic units on a more systematic basis, this section will classify the various losses and show their dependence on the operating variables.

It is generally preferable not to consider overall efficiency, but rather to base the study on a consideration of the torque loss as a function of the operating variables. The torque loss can of course be related to the efficiency by comparing it with the useful power, but there are operating conditions such as open and blocked fluid flow through the unit (the unit producing flow with no pressure or pressure with no flow), where the power produced is zero but the torque loss has a definite practical importance.

Since the usual hydraulic fluids are very nearly in-compressible as far as efficiency is concerned, in this part of the section the fluid will be considered incompressible, and the compressibility effects will be described in part b of this section.

The losses in hydrostatic units can be classified into leakage losses, which represent a loss of flow, and the dry friction, viscous friction and hydrodynamic losses, which properly represent torque loss.

In the following, the principal factors upon which the losses depend will be examined and the actual torque loss and flow will be given as a combination of the principal factors multiplied by dimensionless coefficients. In the formulae for the torques a factor 2π is included to represent the torque losses, although it would have been possible to include this factor in the loss coefficients.

a) *Leakage loss:* From theoretical considerations leakage should be proportional to pressure and inversely proportional to the effective viscosity at the various sealing surfaces. Furthermore, as detailed in section 1.3 c, it will be assumed proportional to the swept volume q_o for geometrically similar units made to the same standard of workmanship.

Therefore

$$Q_s = C_s \frac{\rho}{\mu} q_o \qquad \qquad .. \quad (1.2\text{–}1)$$

In equation (1.2–1) the letter μ refers to the viscosity of the hydraulic fluid at the inlet temperature which is somewhat different from the temperature and viscosity effective at the sealing surfaces, but this is taken into account in the slip coefficient C_s. Since the difference of temperature can vary with the operating variables, the slip coefficient will also be a slowly variable function thereof. Another factor which may account for the lack of constancy of the slip coefficient is that in many designs clearances have a tendency to increase under high pressure and so to leakage increasing more than proportionally with pressure and to the slip coefficient increasing slowly with pressure. On the other hand there are hydrostatic units where leakage increases less than proportionally to pressure which may be due to turbulence or fluid inertia effects in the leakage path. Therefore formula (1.2–1) must be considered only as a first approximation to the actual situation and any deviation can be taken into account by a slowly variable slip coefficient.[1]

The leakage or slip flow may either appear outside the pump as external leakage, where it may be conducted back to the reservoir through an oil cooler if needed or it may find its way back into the admission port and, will then represent internal leakage.

It is also of interest to relate the leakage flow to the increase of displacement to compensate for it, and to the torque which the unit consequently draws from the input shaft:

$$a_s = C_s \frac{p}{\mu n} \qquad \qquad .. \quad (1.2\text{–}2)$$

$$M_s = \frac{C_s}{2\pi} \frac{p^2 q_0}{\mu n} \qquad \qquad .. \quad (1.2\text{–}3)$$

The values on the left hand side of equations (1.2–2) and (1.2–3) are called slip displacement and slip torque, respectively, since they are needed to make up for the slip flow.

From formula (1.2–1) it will be seen that the torque loss required to make up for leakage is proportional to the square of the delivery pressure. This means that with otherwise constant operating variables the power lost by leakage is proportional to the square of the delivery pressure.

---

[1]The use of a slowly variable slip coefficient (and of the other loss coefficients introduced below) is similar to general fluid mechanics, when pressure losses are expressed by the dynamic pressure corresponding to velocity, multiplied by a dimensionless loss coefficient depending on operating variables such as Reynold number.

b) *Dry friction losses:* Dry friction losses are manifest by a torque loss independent of speed and proportional to the internal loads and thus to delivery pressure. They are also proportional to the maximum displacement of the unit but will be considered, as an approximation, as independent of the displacement setting.

Dry friction losses thus also include ball bearing losses. Therefore

$$M_f = \frac{C_f}{2\pi} \rho q_0 \qquad \qquad .. \qquad (1.2\text{--}4)$$

Again it must be noted that the dry friction loss coefficient C_f may depend on the operating variables, and may decrease with increasing shaft speed, because some sliding surfaces may then have metallic contact replaced by an oil wedge action.

c) *Viscous friction:* Viscous friction results from the shearing of the oil film between the many sliding surfaces. The torque loss is directly proportional to the speed and the effective viscosity at the sliding surfaces. For geometrically similar units it is also proportional to their maximum displacement which leads to the following:

$$M_v = \frac{C_v}{2\pi} n\mu q_0 \qquad \qquad .. \qquad (1.2\text{--}5)$$

Strictly speaking some part of the viscous friction is proportional to the displacement setting, e.g. piston friction in piston pumps, but this is to be included in the slow variation of the viscous friction coefficient. For the relation between inlet viscosity and effective viscosity at the sliding surfaces, the same remarks apply as for leakage.

d) *Hydrodynamic losses.* Hydrodynamic losses represent a loss of head or pressure due to fluid flow within the hydrostatic unit. Assuming turbulent conditions along the entire flow path, they result in a pressure loss which is proportional to the mass density of the fluid and to the square of its velocity. The velocity in turn is proportional to shaft speed and displacement setting, and as will be shown below (section 1.3 c) to (displacement)$^{\frac{1}{3}}$. The torque loss is obtained by multiplying this pressure with the actual displacement which leads to the following:—

$$M_h = \frac{C_h}{2\pi} n^2 a^3 I \qquad \qquad .. \qquad (1.2\text{--}6)$$

Where $I = \rho q_o^{5/3}$ can be considered a constant.

The above formula shows that the hydrodynamic torque loss is proportional to the square of the shaft speed and the cube of the displacement setting. It therefore almost vanishes at low shaft speeds and displacement settings.

Since hydrodynamic torque loss is caused by the pressure loss of the fluid flow within hydrostatic units, its magnitude depends on what parts of the actual installation are considered as belonging to the hydrostatic unit, and what parts belong to the piping. In particular it would be possible in a hydrostatic transmission to include the entire piping loss with the hydrodynamical loss in the units. This leads to somewhat increased hydrodynamic loss coefficients but gives the correct dependence on operating variables.

For a rapid assessment of pressure loss in piping, usually sufficient for hydrostatics, this loss can be taken equal to the dynamic pressure of the fluid velocity ($P_{dyn} = \frac{\rho}{2} v^2$) for each 40 diameters length of pipe. At rounded or sharp bends the loss is between 40% to 100% of the dynamic pressure, as described in fluid mechanics text books. Since for a given flow the velocity is inversely proportional to the square of the diameter, and the dynamic pressure is proportional to the square of the velocity, the pressure loss is for given flow and over a given length inversely proportional to the fifth power of the diameter. It therefore increases very rapidly with decreasing diameter of piping.

The leakage losses are responsible for what is usually called volumetric efficiency, and the different torque losses as described constitute the mechanical efficiency.

1.2 B) *Effective torques and flows*

In the preceding part the various sources of loss in a hydrostatic transmission unit were classified and their approximate dependence on operating variables such as speed, pressure etc. were given.

The method of modifying the formulae for flow and torque under loss-less conditions, so as to allow for losses will now be discussed.

It is expedient to use the following expression for the torque loss which is the sum of the dry friction, viscous friction and hydrodynamical torque loss.

$$M_l = \frac{C_f}{2\pi} pq_0 + \frac{C_v}{2\pi} n\mu q_0 + \frac{C_h}{2\pi} n^2 a^3 \, I \qquad .. \qquad (1.2\text{--}7)$$

The following formula giving the flow and torque of a loss-less hydrostatic transmission unit of variable displacement will be used as a basis:

$$Q_0 = nq_0, \quad M_0 = -\frac{pq_0}{2\pi}$$

$$Q_i = naq_0, \quad M_i = -a\frac{\rho q_0}{2\pi} \qquad .. \qquad (1.2\text{--}8)$$

Here a denotes the relative displacement setting, which can vary in most hydrostatic units from $+1$ (full forward) through 0 to -1 (full reverse). The values given by equation (1.2–8) will be referred to as the ideal torque and flow, because they represent an ideal loss—free unit.

In pumping hydrostatic units, the torque loss is negative because it is opposed to speed and it is added to the negative ideal torque to make up the effective torque drawn from the input shaft, and the leakage flow is deducted from the ideal flow to give the effective flow supplied. Therefore

$$M_e = -a\frac{\rho q_0}{2\pi} - M_l \qquad .. \qquad (1.2\text{--}9)$$

$$Q_e = a\,nq_0 - C_s\frac{pq_0}{\mu} \qquad .. \qquad (1.2\text{--}10)$$

Equations (1.2–9) and (1.2–10) give the approximate dependence of the effective torque and flow rate of a hydrostatic unit on operating variables.

It is now desirable to extend the discussion from a pumping unit driven in a certain sense of rotation to a general hydrostatic unit, where shaft speed, torque, displacement, pressure, and flow rate can be reversed or in other words some or all operating variables can become negative or reverse their sign. It is necessary to define the acting pressure as the difference of the pressures at the forward and return ports. Negative effective pressure then means that the return port is under pressure while the pressure in the "forward" port is neglegible. It is necessary to fit non-return valves into both flow lines to prevent cavitation, as will be described in chapter 3.1 in connection with transmission circuits.

The normal operation of the unit, namely pumping into the delivery pipe against pressure will be considered as due to positive operating variables with the exception of the torque which is considered negative because it is opposed to the sense of rotation. From the universal reversibility of hydrostatic units it follows that the equations (1.2–9) and (1.2–10) for torque and flow are also valid, if some or all of the operating variables become negative with the exception of the loss moment which will be discussed presently. This means that the equations also describe correctly the unit when motoring because of reversal of shaft speed as discussed in the introduction, reversal of pressure or displacement.

It will be advantageous to demonstrate the universal applicability of equations (1.2–9) and (1.2–10) for a number of special cases, starting from the normal pumping operation, where all parameters with the exception of torque are positive. One has to imagine that the unit is driven at a selected speed by an external shaft of sufficient power and the pressure in the "forward" port is maintained at the selected value by a sufficiently large accumulator. If the displacement is reversed or made negative the flow and torque will reverse and the unit will be motoring. This is correctly seen from the equation because with negative α, M becomes positive and Q becomes negative. Also the leakage flow which was already negative is now added to the negative ideal flow.

Next suppose that the pressure becomes negative, with displacement still positive, which again results in the unit motoring. From the equation (1.2–9) the torque then becomes positive, i.e. acts in the same sense as the positive rotation, while the ideal flow remains positive and the leakage flow reverses sign and thus becomes added to the ideal flow as it actually is in a motoring unit. Therefore this operating state is also correctly described by equations (1.2–9) and (1.2–10).

Finally there is the case when both displacement and pressure become negative. This can be produced experimentally by reversing the displacement and providing a suitable restrictor in the return line to produce the desired pressure while the non-return valve in the delivery line prevents cavitation. Then the unit is pumping in reverse, since both α and ρ are negative, the moment is still negative and the ideal flow becomes negative. The leakage flow also reverses sign and is therefore subtracted from the ideal flow as it would be in a pumping unit.

It has thus been demonstrated that the equations (1.2–9) and (1.2–10) describe correctly the operation of a hydrostatic unit, with the exception of the torque loss, with one direction of shaft rotation but with either positive or negative pressure or displacement. It is also easy to demonstrate that the same applies to the other direction of shaft rotation, so that the universal applicability of these equations is established.

Referring now to the loss torque M_1 it is always opposed to the direction of rotation and independent of the sign of pressure and displacement. For practical purposes it will be sufficient to remember this, but in appendix A1 a mathematical treatment of the torque loss is developed which gives the correct dependence of the torque loss on the signs of pressure, speed and displacement.

It is interesting to note that the expression for the effective hydraulic and mechanical power converted by a hydrostatic unit is obtained by multiplying equations (1.2–9) and (1.2–10) by speed and pressure respectively:

$$P_{he} = anq_0p - \frac{C_s}{2\pi} \frac{p^2 q_0}{\mu} = anq_0p \left(1 - C_s \frac{p}{n\mu} \frac{1}{a} \right) \qquad .. \quad (1.2\text{–}11)$$

$$P_{me} = -anq_0p - 2\pi nM_1 \qquad .. \qquad .. \qquad .. \quad (1.2\text{–}12)$$

Again equations (1.2–11) and (1.2–12) are valid for any set of positive or negative operating variables for pumping and motoring units. With pumping units negative mechanical power means that the power is entering the mechanical side of the unit, and positive hydraulic power means that power is leaving the unit through the hydraulic system.

Since the power is positive or negative, depending on whether it is absorbed or delivered by the hydrostatic unit, a definition of the efficiency requires special care in order to obtain positive values for the efficiency in normal operation. One way is to define efficiency as the quotient of the absolute values of the powers. A better method is suggested by the observation that in the normal operation of the unit as a mechanical and hydraulic energy converter, one of the powers is always negative because it enters the unit for conversion. Therefore the negative quotient of the powers is a suitable definition yielding positive values of the efficiency, except as mentioned below.

For a pumping unit one obtains as efficiency:

$$\eta = -\frac{P_{he}}{P_{me}} = \frac{1 - C_s p/n\mu a}{1 + 2\pi M_1 a/pq_0} \qquad .. \quad (1.2\text{–}13)$$

There is nothing to prevent the efficiency becoming negative, so indicating that both powers are positive. This could happen, as inspection of equation (1.2–13) shows, with high pressure and with low speed, viscosity, or displacement setting. Physically this means that the pumping unit in this case cannot make up its own leakage and draws part of its leakage from the load instead of supplying it.

Generally the equations (1.2–9) and (1.2–10) are preferred for the effective flow and torque, and equations (1.2–11) and (1.2–12) for power, instead of efficiency, which is mentioned here only for completeness.

An alternative form for the efficiency of a pumping unit is obtained by inserting the expressions for the various torque losses obtained earlier

$$\eta = \frac{1 - C_s p / n \mu a}{1 + C_f / a + C_v \dfrac{n\mu}{p} \dfrac{1}{a} + C_h \, a^2 n I / p q_0} \qquad .. \qquad (1.2\text{--}14)$$

Equation (1.2–14) is only valid for positive values of the operating variables, for the same reasons as mentioned before with the torque loss.

It is to be noted that the efficiency depends both on the displacement setting a and on the design, but only as shown by the loss coefficients. The operating variables determine the efficiency through the following dimensionless parameters $\rho/n\mu$ and $nI/\rho q_0$. The first of these parameters is known from hydrostatic bearing theory and has been introduced in hydraulics by Wilson (see Bibliography 16) and the second parameter by Schloesser (Ref. 1). As it is clear from inspection of equation (1.2–14) and explained in detail in Schloesser's work, the efficiency has an optimum for certain values of the parameters. Such a choice of operating variables for optimum efficiency has a certain intellectual appeal, but limited practical usefulness for hydrostatic units, because they must work with a wide range of speeds, pressures, displacement settings, etc., as part of a variable hydrostatic transmission. It seems more important to ensure that energy loss, including external loss, remains acceptable throughout the whole range. The optimum efficiency will then lie somewhere inside the range.

Ref. 1. W. M. J. Schloesser, Measurements on displacement pumps Thesis, Tech. University, Delft, Holland 1959. (In dutch).

Section 1.2 C

1.2   c) *Reference values of operating variables*

In the preceding treatment of the losses and their dependence on the operating variables, loss coefficients have been introduced, characteristic for the design, giving the magnitude and behaviour of the losses. For many experiments and applications it is more convenient to introduce reference values for the operating variables and to express the actual value of an operating variable at any instant as a multiple or fraction of its reference value.

Both reference speed and reference pressure can be chosen freely, but they are usually selected equal to frequently occuring values e.g. 1 500 rpm and 100 kgf/cm^2 (1 420 psi) for hydrostatic units driven by a.c. electric induction motors.

The reference displacement setting is always equal to the maximum displacement setting of a variable unit giving the same flow as the corresponding fixed displacement unit. The reference flow and reference torque are then given as the flow and torque of a unit with full displacement $a = 1$ running with reference pressure and speed.

The reference values will be noted by the suffix r to the appropriate letter. Thus

$$n_r, \; p_r, \; Q_{or} = n_r q_0, \; M_{or} = \frac{p_r q_0}{2\pi} \qquad .. \quad (1.2\text{--}15)$$

are the reference values of speed, pressure, loss free or ideal flow and torque.

Furthermore it is desirable to introduce reference values for slip flow and torque losses, which are more convenient to handle than the loss coefficients. They are determined from the above reference values of speed and pressure by the following:

$$Q_{sr} = C_s \frac{p_r}{\mu} q_0, \qquad M_{fr} = \frac{C_f}{2\pi} p_r q_0$$

$$\qquad\qquad\qquad\qquad\qquad .. \quad (1.2\text{--}16)$$

$$M_{vr} = \frac{C_v}{2\pi} n_r \mu q_0, \qquad M_{hr} = \frac{C_h}{2\pi} n_r^2 I$$

The actual values of the slip flow and torque losses at any set of operating variables can now be expressed as multiples of the reference values defined by equation (1.2–16).

3

$$Q_s = \frac{p}{p_r} Q_{sr} \qquad M_f = \frac{p}{p_r} M_{fr}$$

$$M_v = \frac{n}{n_r} M_{vr} \qquad M_h = a^3 \frac{n^2}{n_r{}^2} M_{hr} \qquad \cdots \quad (1.2\text{--}17)$$

The equation (1.2–17) is equivalent to the equations (1.2–1), (1.2–4), (1.2–5) and (1.2–6) but incorporating the reference values instead of the loss coefficients. For completeness and in analogy to equations (1.2–2) and (1.2–3) the slip displacement and the slip torque will also be given here with reference values, obtained by simple algebraic manipulation with equation (1.2–15) to (1.2–17).

$$a_s = \frac{p}{p_r} \frac{n_r}{n} \frac{Q_{sr}}{Q_{or}}$$

$$\frac{M_s}{M_{or}} = \frac{p}{p_r} a_s = \left(\frac{\rho}{\rho_r}\right)^2 \frac{n_r}{n} \frac{Q_{sr}}{Q_{or}} \qquad \cdots \quad (1.2\text{--}18)$$

For the effective torque and flow one obtains, instead of equations (1.2–9) and (1.2–10)

$$M_e = -M_{or}\left(a\frac{p}{p_r} + \frac{M_l}{M_{or}}\right) \qquad \cdots \quad (1.2\text{--}19)$$

$$Q_e = Q_{or}\left(a\frac{n}{n_r} - \frac{p}{p_r}\frac{Q_{sr}}{Q_{or}}\right) \qquad \cdots \quad (1.2\text{--}20)$$

By inserting values for the various torque losses of equation (1.2–17) one obtains for the total torque losses, using reference variables

$$M_e = -M_{or}\left(a\frac{p}{p_r} + \frac{p}{p_r}\frac{M_{fr}}{M_{or}} + \frac{n}{n_r}\frac{M_{vr}}{M_{or}} + a^3\frac{n^2}{n_r{}^2}\frac{M_{hr}}{M_{or}}\right) \quad (1.2\text{--}21)$$

The practical value of equations (1.2–19), (1.2–20) and (1.2–21) lies in the fact that they express effective flows and torques from the slip flow and torque losses in the reference values of the operating variables, where they can be easily measured.

As an example with a typical hydrostatic unit, at the reference pressure $p_r = 100$ kgf/cm^2 (1 420 psi) and speed $n_r = 1\,500$ rpm, leakage is 1%, dry and viscous friction each 1%, hydrodynamic loss 2% of the reference flow and torque. This allows us to write equations (1.2–19) and (1.2–20), using also equation (1.2–21), as follows

$$Q_e = Q_{or}\left(a\frac{n}{n_r} - \frac{p}{p_r}\frac{1}{100}\right)$$

$$M_e = -M_{or}\left(a\frac{p}{p_r} + \frac{p}{p_r}\frac{1}{100} + \frac{n}{n_r}\frac{1}{100} + a^3\frac{n^2}{n_r^2}\frac{2}{100}\right) \qquad (1.2\text{–}22)$$

This equation is a practical formula for the determination of effective flow and torque from the operating variables. The loss torques alone are given in this example by:

$$M_l = M_{or}\left(\frac{\rho}{\rho_r}\frac{1}{100} + \frac{n}{n_r}\frac{1}{100} + a^3\frac{n^2}{n_r^2}\frac{2}{100}\right) \qquad \ldots \qquad (1.2\text{–}23)$$

The introduction of the reference speed, pressure, torque and flow has the effect of simplifying calculations which occur in practice for the determination of performance and efficiency of a hydrostatic transmission. The reference values of slip flow and torque losses are usually determined by a separate experiment. Similar reference values are also used in the theory of automatic speed governing of water turbines (see Hutarew Bibliography 11).

d) *Compressibility effects*

So far, the working fluid has been considered incompressible, but in this part the effect of finite compressibility on operation and efficiency of hydrostatic units will be treated. The relative volume change of hydraulic fluid on application of pressure is given by

$$\frac{\Delta V}{V^1} = \frac{P}{B} \qquad \ldots \qquad (1.2\text{–}24)$$

The compressibility modulus B depends on the type of hydraulic fluid and is affected by small air inclusions. A typical value of B for reasonably well deaerated fluid is 15 000 kgf/cm² (214 000 psi), giving a relative volume change of 1% for an applied pressure of 150 kgf/cm² (2 200 psi).

Since the fluid compresses on pressure application and expands on
pressure release, the volume flow for a given mass or quantity flow
depends to a small extent on pressure. The volume flow will now be
defined as measured under pressure, because this flow is responsible
for the approach speed of loaded rams etc. In many experiments with
pumping units, the flow meter is placed downstream of the relief or
pressure setting valve, and a suitable correction has to be made.

The working cycle of a pumping unit is represented in fig.
1.2–1 using ideal valving, i.e. operating at the correct moments.

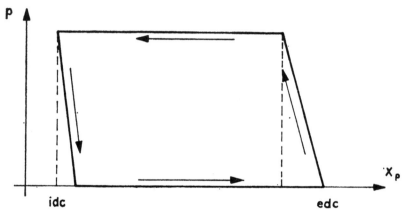

1.2–1 Working cycle of displacement unit with compressible fluid and
switching volume at dead centres

Beginning at external dead centre (edc) the piston travels inward,
compresses fluid with consequent pressure rise. When delivery
pressure is reached, connection to delivery port is established and
fluid delivered with further piston movement inwards. At internal
dead centre (idc) the delivery port is sealed and the piston starts to
travel outwards. Since there is some volume left in the cylinder at
idc, pressure does not fall instantly, but fairly rapidly as shown on
the figure. When pressure in the cylinder has fallen to intake pressure, the intake port is opened and the piston draws in fluid with
further outward travel, until at edc the cycle recommences. The
piston force is equal to the instantaneous pressure multiplied by the
piston surface. In a motoring unit the same cycle is run through in
reverse.

The cycle shown on fig. 1.2–1 is operated with ideal valving, that is
the valving always establishes connection to intake and delivery port
at the correct position. Since this correct position depends on delivery

pressure and displacement setting it is difficult to achieve in hydrostatic units with positive valving. Pumping units with non-return valves have ideal valving at low speeds, whilst at high speed the inertia of the moving valve parts interferes with the correct timing.

If valving establishes connections at any other position, e.g. at exactly dead centres, fluid rushes in the cylinder from the delivery port to compress the fluid already there, and is then expelled by the movement of the piston. As far as volume and flow are concerned, the position is the same as with ideal valving, but the piston has now to supply the full force to expel the fluid, instead of the gradually increasing compression force. Instead of an expansion stroke, the fluid rushes from the cylinder to the inlet port with dead centre valving. Again volume remains unchanged, but no force is exerted by the piston instead of the former rapidly decreasing expansion force which has driven the piston outward, supplying mechanical work. Thermal effects, so important in the theory of gases, are neglected because they are small in fluids.

The effect of compressibility on flow is that some extra fluid is taken in at each compression stroke or pressure increase in the cylinder from the delivery port, independent of the design of valving. What happens during fall of pressure in the cylinder, whether through expansion or exhausting into the intake port is irrelevant to the flow in the high pressure or delivery conduit.

From the above description of the working cycle it is seen that some fluid is needed to compress the fluid already contained in the cylinder at the moment of switching from the low to the high pressure ports. This is given by equation (1.2–24), where V^1 is the volume of the cylinder and ports at the switching point. If the unit has z cylinders each operating once every revolution, the flow is:

$$Q_c = nzV^1 \frac{p}{B} \qquad \cdot \cdot \quad (1.2\text{--}25)$$

Figure 1.2–2 shows a cylinder of an axial piston hydrostatic unit with piston in mid stroke with the dead centre positions depending on the stroke (indicated by dotted lines).

In variable stroke piston units, the stroke is proportional to the displacement setting a and the switching volume is given by

$$V^1 = V_{re} + \frac{V_0}{2}(1+a) \qquad \cdot \cdot \quad (1.2\text{--}26)$$

where V_{re} is the residual volume in cylinder and ports at idc and maximum stroke, and V_0 is the displacement of the cylinder with $a = 1$. The preceding equation applies both to pumping units, where the switching from low to high pressure takes place at edc, and to motoring units where it takes place at idc, with a negative as mentioned in section 1.2–c.

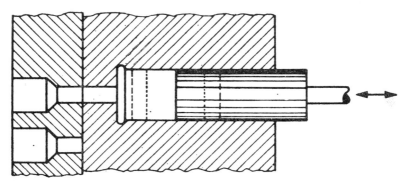

1.2-2 Scheme of variable stroke piston unit with dead centres depending on displacement setting

Combining equation 1.2–25 and 1.2–26 one obtains with $q_0 = zV_0$

$$Q_c = nq_0 \frac{p}{B} \left(\frac{V_{re}}{V_0} + \frac{1+a}{2} \right) \qquad .. \quad (1.2\text{–}27)$$

This can be represented as

$$Q_c = C_c \, nq_0 \frac{p}{B} \qquad .. \quad (1.2\text{–}28)$$

where the compressibility loss coefficient depends principally on a. Since in axial piston hydrostatic units, V_{re}/V_0 is usually about $\frac{1}{4}$, it is given by

$$C_c = \frac{3}{4} + \frac{a}{2} \qquad .. \quad (1.2\text{–}29)$$

As it is seen from equations (1.2–28) and (1.2–29), the practical magnitude of the compressibility flow at 150 kgf/cm² is 1.25% for pumping and $\frac{1}{4}$% for a motoring unit at full displacement.

The compressibility flow Q_c appears as a flow defect in the delivery when measured at the working pressure. It is proportional to the pressure and has the character of a leakage flowing from the high to low pressure ports. Unlike leakage it is proportional to the rotative speed, independent of the viscosity and depends on the displacement setting. The compressibility flow does not appear outside as part of leakage does, but since mass is conserved, part of it reappears on expansion of the delivered fluid, and the rest is returned to the intake ports when the cylinder is switched back from high to low pressure.

Turning now to the energy relations, the power loss connected with the compressibility flow depends on the details of valving of the hydrostatic unit. If in a hydrostatic transmission valving is ideal, compression and expansion take place as shown in fig. 1.2–1 and no energy is lost. In the most unfavourable case, with dead centre valving, the entire power given by compressibility flow and pressure is lost. Ideal valving with consequent correct compression and expansion can thus save 1.25% of the power of the pumping and $\frac{1}{4}\%$ of the motoring unit at full displacement with a pressure of 150 kgf /cm^2 (2 150 psi) and proportionally more at higher pressures. The valving needed for correct compression and expansion depends not only on pressure, but also on displacement setting and is therefore exceedingly difficult to achieve in practice. Nevertheless, the compression losses are among the factors that ultimately limit the practical operating pressures of hydrostatic transmissions.

With the numerical values mentioned, compressibility flow is comparable to the magnitude of the leakage.

In spite of its different characteristics, it is included in the leakage as an engineering approximation and in particular, the leakage cofficient derived by equation (1.2–1), includes the compressibility flow effect.

Section 1.3

a) *Performance of hydrostatic units*

Hydrostatic units convert shaft speed and torque into flow and pressure, while energy may travel in either direction. Naturally there are limits to what a hydrostatic unit can handle and in this section the nature of these limits will be discussed.

The determining dimension of a hydrostatic unit is the maximum displacement or swept volume, denoted by q_o which is proportional

to the cube of the linear size of a given model, and this is treated
in more detail in section 1.3 c.

For a hydrostatic unit with a given swept volume, the power
is proportional to the pressure and to the shaft speed, as can be
seen from the fundamental equations (1.1–2) and (1.1–3.) It is always
desirable to obtain as much power as possible from a given unit,
therefore both pressure and shaft speed will be selected as high as
possible but they must not exceed certain values in order to avoid
unreliability and short life.

The principal limit for shaft speed is that the sliding velocities
which are directly proportional thereto should not become so high
as to incur the danger of seizing and of overheating.

The limit on pressure comes from the fact that all loads and
bending moments are directly proportional thereto. Therefore
certain values of pressure particular to each design of hydrostatic
unit must not be exceeded in order to obtain a sufficiently long
fatigue life. Some hydrostatic units are equipped with ball and
roller bearings where the load does not have a rigid boundary, but
where the life decreases with the cube of the continuous load.
Unfortunately the calculated lives of ball bearings, are only average
for a large quantity of bearings, and the actual life of individual
bearings is subject to large deviations, as is well known from the
literature on ball bearings. There are several other components in
hydrostatic units that behave similarly to ball bearings as far as
life is concerned.

Hydrostatic bearings, lubricated by pressure oil supplied by the
hydrostatic unit itself are operated without any load limit, because
lubricating pressure increases proportionally to delivery pressure.
With very high sliding velocities however, they tend to become
unreliable due to local overheating. A factor which limits the
admissable load on hydrostatic plain bearings is the deformation of
the support, proportional to load, which may distort the oil film
and even lead to metallic contact at some points, which will result
in overheating and seizing.

Summarizing the effect of pressure and speed, it can be said that
they are not strict limits for a given design of hydrostatic unit but
depend on the life and on the reliability required. Naturally they
depend on the design of the hydrostatic units, and there are some
designs more suited to high speed or pressure.

Of quite a different nature are the limits on operating conditions
due to efficiency considerations. Again they do depend on the
detailed design of the hydrostatic unit under consideration, but the
following remarks apply generally.

With increasing shaft speed hydrodynamic or flow losses become
relatively more prominent as seen from equation (1.2–6) or (1.2–17)
and tend to depress the efficiency. Furthermore, since hydrodynamic losses come from the pressure loss due to the flow within
the unit, zero pressure and cavitation have to be avoided by higher
priming pressure in units running at very high speed. For simple
self-priming hydrostatic units used in an open circuit as described
in section 3.1, the danger of cavitation has a very definite limit on
speed which is usually lower than the speed limit due to the sliding
velocities.

Some extension of the speed range is obtained by ensuring that
the highest rotative speeds are only used with reduced displacement
as it is the case when driving a motoring unit from a constant flow
source. Thus the hydronamic or flow losses are maintained within
acceptable limits because the flow is limited. In the case of self-
priming units, limiting the maximum displacement is a very
effective and sometimes practical method of extending the speed
range without danger of cavitation.

Another justification for admitting higher rotative speeds with
reduced displacement is that some sliding velocities such as piston
speed are proportional to displacement, and the sliding velocities
of the pistons are thus limited. On the other hand some sliding
velocities are unaffected by the displacement setting, as for instance
the velocity of the valve faces in axial piston pumps which must be
able to withstand sufficiently high velocities.

The maximum pressure is also limited by efficiency consideration,
because the energy losses due to leakage, as given by equation
(1.2–4) are proportional to the square of the pressure. Since the useful power increases only proportionally to pressure, the relative
energy loss due to leakage is again proportional to pressure and will
therefore become intolerable at very high pressures.

The efficiency of a hydrostatic unit also becomes poor at very low
speeds and pressures, because the relative importance of either
leakage and dry friction or the other torque losses becomes excessive.
Between both there is a region of optimum efficiency, as has been
discussed in a very elegant way by Dr. Schloesser [1].

Furthermore very low efficiencies are also obtained with low displacement settings ($a << 1$). With zero pressure, no flow due to
diminishing displacement ($a = 0$) or a stationary shaft, efficiency is
zero because no work is done. This may be thought a singular operating condition but it is sometimes required in the operation of hydrostatic transmissions. Although the efficiency is zero, the power

[1]See Ref. 1 page 34

consumption to produce pressure without flow or flow without pressure is of great practical importance, as will be seen in sections 2.3 and 3.3.

b) *Flow ripple in piston units*

In hydrostatic displacement units, the instantaneous delivery or output flow is given by the rate of reduction of the displacement volumes while connected to the delivery line. If the displacement rate is not uniform, periodic variation of the instantaneous delivery flow, or flow ripple, occurs. Because of its practical importance, the characteristics and magnitudes of variation of instantaneous delivery with drive shaft position or flow ripple for multicylinder piston pumps of any design, including axial piston pumps is discussed below.

In a piston pump the rate of change of the displacement volume is given by the piston velocity during the delivery stroke. Since in most piston pumps the piston position is a harmonic or simple sine function of the shaft rotative position to a very near approximation, the piston velocity and thus the instantaneous delivery is a sine function of the rotative position of the drive shaft.

It is expedient to consider first the delivery of a single acting single cylinder pump. Here the term single acting denotes a design feature common to most hydrostatic piston pumps, namely that only one endface of the piston is working in contact with the pressure fluid. Discussion in this book will always refer to single-acting pistons, unless stated otherwise.

Referring to fig. 1.3–1 the instantaneous delivery of a single cylinder piston pump is represented as a function of the drive shaft position, beginning at the outer dead centre. The flow is a sine curve, reaching its maximum at midstroke and returning to zero at inner dead centre, after a rotation of 180° of the drive shaft. During the next half rotation of the drive shaft from 180 to 360°, no delivery occurs, because the piston returns while connected to the inlet port. After a complete revolution of the shaft the delivery begins again. The delivery flow of a single cylinder piston pump has thus the aspect of a rectified sine curve as obtained by half wave rectification of an ac electric current.

In analogy to electrical engineering it is indicated to use a phasor representation of the delivery as shown on fig. 1.3–2. Here the phasor is in uniform rotation with the shaft speed, and the instantaneous delivery is proportional to its projection on the vertical axis, between the shaft angles of 0 and 180°. During the second half revolution the phasor collapses, or contributes nothing to delivery as shown in

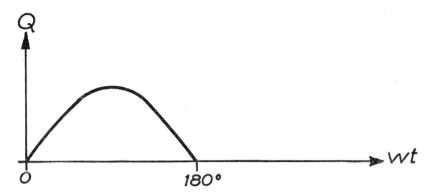

1.3-1 Instantaneous delivery of one single acting cylinder as function of shaft angle

the figure. It should be noted, that the phasor contributes to delivery only as long as it points upwards.

Turning now to multicylinder pumps, the phasor representation is especially useful. The treatment will be restricted to multicylinder pumps, where the dead centres of the piston movement are distributed uniformly over the drive shaft position. This is the only case of practical interest and axial and radial piston pumps with the cylinders uniformly distributed radially around the cylinder block belong to this class. To each cylinder a phasor describing its instantaneous delivery is allocated, and the total delivery is determined from the vectorial addition of the phasor. Due to the uniform distribution of piston movements, the phasors have a constant angle between each other, this angle being $2\pi/z$ where z is the number of cylinders. It is known from elementary geometry and can be shown easily by drawing, that all phasors form an z sided regular polygon, the arrow of the last phasor joining the origin of the first phasor. The regular

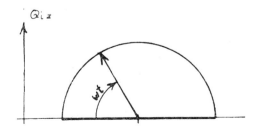

1.3-2 Phasor representation of delivery of a single cylinder

polygons formed by the phasors is represented in fig. 1.3–3 for a 5-cylinder pump in two rotative positions.

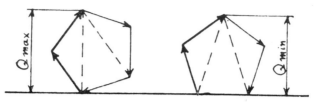

1.3-3 Polygon built from the phasors representing multi-cylinder delivery

As mentioned above, the phasors contribute to delivery only if they are pointing upwards, that is if their phase angle is between the limits of 0 and 180°. Such phasors are drawn in heavy line in fig. 1.3–3. The total instantaneous delivery of a multicylinder pump is therefore proportional to the maximum extension of the polygon— along the vertical axis, or of the height of a relevant polygon rolling on a horizontal plane. This is shown in fig. 1.3–3 for 2 rotative positions corresponding to maximum and minimum delivery. In the case of an odd number of cylinders (z odd) maximum delivery occurs when one of the diagonals shown dotted is vertical, and minimum delivery when the two dotted diagonals shown are arranged symmetrically around the vertical. Using this geometric diagram the actual flow ripple can be calculated by a simple trigonometric formula, but it is interesting to examine first the differences between odd and even numbers of cylinders.

The polygon of phasors representing instantaneous delivery is valid both for odd and even number of cylinders, and the different flow ripple derives from the difference of the geometries of regular polygons with an odd or even number of sides. As far as rolling of the relevant polygons on a plane or flow ripple is concerned, an odd polygon can be thought of as a part of an even polygon having double the number of sides (fig. 1.3–4). In effect, the rolling of the large even polygon of fig. 1.3–4 is identical to two small odd polygons rolling in the relative position shown in the plane. Since in this relative position the fluctuations of both small odd polygons are in phase and additive, the fluctuation of one odd polygon has the same characteristics and the same relative magnitude compared to average delivery. We have therefore established the important fact that the flow ripple or relative variation of instanteous delivery compared to average delivery of an odd number of cylinder piston pumps is identical to that of a piston pump having double the number of cylinders. Thus the flow ripple of a 5 cylinder pump is identical to the one of a 10 cylinder pump and less than that of a 6 and 8 cylinder pump, and the flow ripple of a 7 cylinder pump is identical to that of a 14 cylinder pump and smaller than the flow ripple of a 10 and 12 cylinder pump. Since the geometry of an even sided polygon is somewhat simpler, it is usually expedient to compute the flow ripple of odd cylinder pumps by computing that of the corresponding pump having double the number of cylinders.

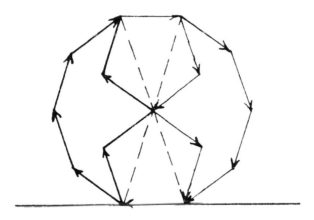

1.3–4 Polygons showing the equality of delivery flow ripple from a pump with an odd number of cylinders to that from a pump with double number of cylinders

From the polygon diagrams it is also seen that the number of flow variations per shaft revolution is 2 z for odd number cylinders and z for even number cylinders. Thus in the case of 7 cylinder pumps the flow fluctuates 14 times per shaft revolution. From the trigonometry of the triangle formed by the broken line diagonals and the horizontal line of the polygon in fig. 1.3–4 one obtains the following formula for the relative flow variation:

$$\frac{Q_{max}-Q_{min}}{Q_{max}} = 1-\cos \pi/2z = 1-\cos 90°/z \quad \text{(z odd)} \qquad (1.3–1)$$

$$= 1-\cos \pi/z \quad = 1-\cos 180°/z \quad \text{(z even)}$$

Actual values for the flow ripple taken from this formula are given in table 1.3–1.

Table 1.3–1

Flow ripple in multicylinder pumps

Z =	1	2	3	4	5	6	7	8	9	10	11	
$\dfrac{Q_{max} - Q_{min}}{Q_{max}}$ =	100		13,4		4,9		2,5		1,5		1,0	per cent
=		100		29,3		13,5		7,6		4,9		per cent

The above considerations and the numerical values in the table illustrate the much smaller flow ripple for pumps with an odd number of cylinders. Since the flow ripple is a principal cause of vibrations and other nuisances, it is obviously desirable to keep it as small as possible and this is the reason why most actual piston pumps have an odd number of cylinders.

While the geometric reasoning presented here gives all necessary information with a minimum of mathematics, it is also possible to make a Fourier analysis of the delivery of one cylinder or of the curve of fig. 1.3–1. This gives the content of higher harmonics of a single cylinder pump. For multicylinder pumps it is then possible to add the coefficients of the harmonics, taking into account their phase relationship. After some mathematic manipulation it is seen, that for odd number of cylinders all harmonics cancel up to the order 2 z and that the remaining harmonics are identical to that of a pump having 2 z (z odd) cylinders, in accordance with the geometric results above. This analysis is very illustrative and may be left as an exercise for the interested reader.

Finally as a word of caution to the experimenter, it should be mentioned that delivery fluctuation is not proportional nor corresponding to pressure fluctuation. In effect, the harmonic components of the delivery fluctuations excite in the load different magnitudes of pressure fluctuation depending on its characteristics with usually many reasonance possibilities due to the actual load. Therefore the picture taken on a pressure transducer will generally not correspond with the delivery fluctuation.

This analysis is also valid for other than piston pumps, as long as delivery from a number of displacement chambers, spaced uniformly around the drive shaft and having a single rectified sine delivery curve. If the displacement chamber does not vary according to a sine curve, it is possible to make a Fourier analysis of this, giving the sine curve as fundamental and the deviations thereof as higher harmonics. Then the polygon construction can be made for the fundamental and each higher harmonic of significant magnitude, but this is of too little practical importance to justify description here.

The flow ripple of a pumping unit driven with uniform speed is equal to the torque ripple of a motoring unit fed with uniform or constant pressure.

c) Model laws

Many designs of hydrostatic units especially axial piston pumps, are produced in several sizes as a series of scale enlargements of a basic model. The permissible shaft speeds decrease with size but pressure remains unaffected. The scale or model laws of a given design are therefore of interest.

The discussion will be based on the linear scale factor L which gives the increase or decrease of length from a basic model for the size under consideration.

Then all areas, sections of flow passages, pistons surfaces etc. are proportional to L^2, and all volumes, especially the swept volume or maximum displacement q_o are proportional to L^3.

Velocities including sliding velocities of parts in relative motion and flow velocity are proportional to the length L and to the shaft speed. All loads are proportional to L^2 and to pressure. Moments, especially bending moments are produced from loads multiplied by the length of leverage and are therefore proportional to L^3 and pressure. Stresses due to loads and bending moments are independent of size (since the moment of resistence is proportional to L^3) and proportional to pressure.

Thus permissible pressure is independent of size while shaft speed, limited by sliding and flow velocities is inversely proportional to linear size, $n \sim 1/L$ or $n \sim 1/q_o^{\frac{1}{3}}$. In other words, larger units must run slower but can produce the same pressure.

Centrifugal forces in hydrostatic units are normally unimportant compared with pressure forces. They are proportional to the mass and the radius of the particular member and to the square of shaft speed. Since mass is proportional to L^3, centrifugal forces are proportional to $L^4 n^2$. If shaft speed is reduced with increasing size to maintain velocity constant, $n \sim 1/L$ centrifugal forces are proportional to L^2, as are pressure loads, and consequently the resultant stresses are independent of size.

Furthermore it is of interest to establish model laws for the different forms of losses. For leakage, it is reasonable to base the discussion

on the known formula for viscous flow between parallel plates, which
is representative for most sealing surfaces (see Ernst, Bibliography 4,
equa 5.16).

$$Q_s = \frac{1}{12} \frac{p}{\mu} \frac{b}{L} \delta^3 \qquad \qquad .. \quad (1.3\text{--}2)$$

When scaling a given design, b/L remains constant as the ratio of
two lengths. So that the slip flow is proportional to the maximum
displacement, δ^3 must be proportional to q_o, or δ proportional to the
length L. Naturally, clearance does depend on a number of factors
which are, together with the minimum admissible clearance for safe
running, the subject of hydrodynamic and hydrostatic bearing
theory. (See Fuller Bibliography 5). However, as first approximation
the clearance δ can be considered proportional to the length or linear
dimensions, which result in a slip flow proportional to the maximum
displacement, as stated previously.

From the manufacturing standpoint it is possible to increase the
clearance rather less rapidly than in direct proportion to the length
or cube of the displacement. Indeed the units of tolerance, as given
by the international standard association, are proportional to the
cube root of the length, up to nominal sizes of several feet. For equal
manufacturing standards, clearance should be a multiple of the
tolerance unit, proportional to the cube root of the length, thus increasing very slowly with increasing size of the hydrostatic unit.

It should be mentioned that the ISA system of tolerances is now
also used with the inch system (B.S.1916:1953).

From the manufacturing tolerance point of view it would be possible to provide clearances increasing very slowly with size, but
considering the heating of sliding surfaces and the deformation of the
parts it is still preferable to increase clearances proportionally to the
length.

For a range of similar hydrostatic units running at the same speed,
leakage is proportional to the maximum displacement. Furthermore,
viscous and dry friction torque, being proportional to the area of the
sliding surfaces and its distance from the axis, increase proportionally
to maximum displacement. On the other hand, the hydrodynamical
torque loss, being dependent on the flow velocity, increases more rapidly than length because of the dependence of the factor I in equation (1.2–6) on maximum displacement.

If the speed is decreased with size in order to leave sliding and
fluid velocities constant the relative importance of leakage increases,
since it is approximately independent of speed. This can partly be

compensated by making the clearances smaller, but the effect of this depends too much on the individual case to allow of a general statement.

The same applies to viscous friction, whilst dry friction and hydrodynamical losses remain unchanged. Summarizing the effect of scale reduction on losses; both leakage flow for a constant pressure and torque losses, when speeds are reduced with size to keep sliding velocities constant, are approximately proportional to the maximum displacement q_o, or the cube of the length.

Consequently the power lost through leakage at a fixed pressure and the power lost through dry and viscous friction at reduced speed are nearly proportional to maximum displacement. Strictly viscous friction increases only slowly, being proportional to $q_o^{2/3}$, but may be considered as approximately proportional to the maximum displacement q_o.

Section 1.4

Experiments with hydrostatic units

In this section several possible experiments and tests with hydrostatic units will be discussed. As with all advanced machinery, experiments with hydrostatic units are important not only for development, but also as acceptance tests for users wishing to choose between competing makers.

Many interesting experiments can be performed on hydrostatic units with comparatively simple test installations because hydrostatic units are extremely versatile. This is because the displacement can be varied and in consequence the flow delivered by pumping units can be selected at any value with constant shaft speed. The pressure produced depends on the restriction placed in the delivery line, either a simple adjustable restrictor or a relief valve with adjustable setting. Thus any desired amount of flow and any desired pressure can be produced by a simple installation with constant shaft speed.

In this section the following tests on a hydrostatic unit driven at constant speed will be described:

a) Full power efficiency and functional test.

b) Cycling test with accumulator.

c) Open and blocked port experiments.

It should be mentioned that in industry the simplest variable speed test installation is a hydrostatic transmission driven by an

4

induction electric motor to which the hydrostatic unit under test is coupled for variable speed tests. This is usually more convenient than a variable speed DC electric motor and has the advantage of testing the hydrostatic transmission at the same time. Such an installation is shown on figure 3.4–2a and be further discussed in section 3.4.

a) *Full power test*

In the simplest experiment a hydrostatic unit is driven at constant speed and pumps oil against a restrictor. Flow is varied by adjusting the displacement setting of the pump and the pressure is selected by setting the restrictor. The restrictor can be either a variable throttling device such as a needle valve, which has to be reset after each change of flow, or a continuously blowing relief valve where the pressure is much less dependent on flow. In order to avoid a sudden stoppage due to dirt, with consequent damage by pressure surges an additional safety valve in the delivery pipe is recommended. This simple experiment is essentially a test under constant operating conditions, with only infrequent manual adjustments of flow and pressure.

It is normally used only as a preliminary test to prove the correct operation of the hydrostatic unit.

It is good practice on all tests to monitor continuously the quantity and temperature of the leakage oil, since any immediate danger of seizing can usually be detected by a sudden increase of temperature of the leakage oil before too much damage is done. In many axial piston pumps, the difference in temperature between the leakage and inlet oil corresponds to the heat equivalent of the energy of expanding the fluid itself, that is 5.5°c per 100 kgf/cm^2 (10° F per 1 420 psi) delivery pressure.

The experiment under full power can be also used to determine the efficiency of a hydrostatic unit, by measuring the outlet oil flow and pressure and the driving torque and speed. This is very simply done, usually by placing a calibrated flow meter downstream of the restrictor.

The efficiency is then computed by the following formula:

$$\eta = \frac{1}{2\pi} \frac{Q.p}{Mn} \qquad .. \quad (1.4\text{--}1)$$

Strictly speaking, a correction has to be applied for the compressibility of the oil, described in section 1.2–c, but this is often neglected.

The above method of determining efficiency is not very accurate because of the difficulty of measuring with sufficient accuracy the four separate terms (flow, pressure, speed and torque).

The theory of errors shows that if each of the four values is measured with an accuracy of $\pm 2\%$, which may just be attainable with a simple apparatus, the accuracy of the efficiency figure is $\pm 8\%$. In other words; if the true efficiency at a particular point is 94% then the result from the measurements will lie between 86% and 102% which is necessarily of little value for high efficiency units. In order to obtain useful information, the accuracy of the measurements must be increased by at least a factor of 10. Such precision measurements are very difficult, but they have been made by the National Engineering Laboratory, East Kilbride, Scotland and the reader interested in precision measurements is referred to the relevant NEL publication (ref. 1).

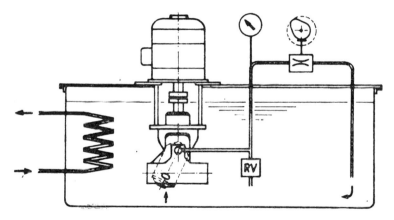

1.4–1 Scheme of cycling test of hydrostatic unit with constant power actuator delivering against cam-operated restrictor

A useful variation of the full power experiment is a cycling test, as represented schematically on fig. 1.4–1. Here the hydrostatic unit, driven by an electric AC motor, suspended vertically in a tank is equipped with a constant power actuator. The actuator reduces pump displacement at higher pressures by balancing a small piston fed with delivery pressure against a spring with variable characteristics, in such a way that the product of flow and pressure, and therefore

Ref. 1 W.H.P. Leslie, Precision Dynamometer, Proc. 1st I.C.I.F.A.C. Butterworth London 1960.

the power, remains approximately constant. The restriction in the delivery line is continuously varied by a cam rotating slowly and thereby changing the setting of the restrictor. In a typical arrangement the cam is driven from a small electric motor through a worm reduction at 6 cycles per minute, and the restrictor and constant power controller are dimensioned so that the pressure oscillates between 100 kgf/cm² (1 420 psi) and 250 kgf/cm² (3 600 psi). A relief valve and an oil cooler are included for protection.

This cycling test has the advantage of testing the unit pumping at different flows and pressures and thus simulating more closely actual operation. A cycle repetition frequency of 6 cpm is also a comparatively severe test of the swivel bearings and trunnions. This arrangement is therefore frequently used in development and endurance tests.

A common disadvantage of all full power experiments is that the entire power is wasted, causing excessive power cost and making it necessary to provide sufficient cooling capacity and this test becomes impractical for more than about 30 HP.

It is possible to separate the different components of losses in the full power test, although for this purpose the open and blocked port test of section 1.4–c is more suitable. The separation of losses is effectuated with reference to the equations (1.2–9) and (1.2–10). In particular, the reduction of flow with pressure gives the total leakage. If with increasing delivery pressure the shaft speed is slightly reduced due to the prime mover slowing down a suitable correction must be made. This is normally necessary with hydrostatic units driven at full displacement by AC induction motors due to the speed slip with increasing torque.

The total torque loss M_i is obtained by deducting from the effective torque the ideal torque which is a function of pressure and displacement setting. In order to obtain the different torque losses separately one first measures with no delivery pressure. The torque with zero displacement setting is that due to viscous friction and with full displacement setting the sum of viscous friction and hydrodynamical losses. The increase of the total torque loss with applied pressure then gives the dry friction torque.

Naturally the numerical values obtained will vary somewhat, because of the approximate nature of the loss formulae, and because of the slow variation of the loss coefficients with the operating variables. In consequence it is desirable to prepare several determinations of the loss coefficients at different values of the operating variables and adopt as final values those that are closest to the mean of the experimental points.

b) *Cycling test with accumulator*

In order to reduce power consumption in a cycling test, it is possible to use the pumping unit to charge an accumulator using an arrangement as shown in fig. 1.4–2.

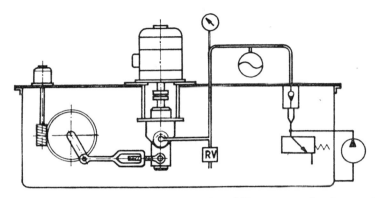

1.4–2 Cycling test of hydrostatic unit with delivery controller by crank, delivering into an accumulator

In this experiment the displacement of a self priming hydrostatic unit is continuously and automatically varied from forward ($a>0$) to the reverse ($a<0$) to give the average displacement of nearly zero.

When pumping the hydrostatic unit delivers into the accumulator and after reversal it draws fluid from it thereby motoring and returning the energy to the drive shaft. The pressure in the delivery line and accumulator varies according to the pump flow, accumulator capacity and cycling frequency. A relief valve is needed to set an upper limit and a non-return valve backed by priming pressure to set a lower limit to the system pressure. Instead of priming pressure atmospheric pressure can be used by submerging the non-return valve. The practical arrangement of the cycling test with accumulator is shown in fig. 1.4–2. Here the displacement of the hydrostatic unit is continuously varied by connecting the actuating pivot on the unit by a tie rod to a slowly rotating crank, driven through a worm reduction gear from a small electric motor. For convenience it is desirable to have the crank radius and the length of the tie rod adjustable so that the amplitude and the average value of the displacement can be varied. A typical cycling frequency is 120 cpm.

This is a very severe test on the hydrostatic unit because it is alternately pumping and motoring and because of the continuous and comparatively rapid variation of displacement. The power consumption is very low, because with reverse displacement the unit is driving the electric motor which returns electric power to the main electricity supply. Heat production is comparatively low, but it is advisable to check periodically the temperature in the delivery line. The author has used this severe test when developing hydrostatic units with a saving on electricity costs, using a pressure swing from 100 kgf/cm² (1 420 psi) to 250 kgf/cm² (3 500 psi). It is also very hard on the accumulator, but the gas loaded bladder type accumulator manufactured under Greer Mercier patents in many countries of the world seem to be able to withstand this treatment for thousands of hours.

c) *Open and blocked port experiments*

Further interesting experiments with hydrostatic units are possible by varying the displacement. They consist of measurements on the hydrostatic unit when rotating at normal speed first with unrestricted delivery and then with completely obstructed delivery. They are analogeous to open and shortcircuit measurements on DC machines in electrical engineering.

The installation necessary is extremely simple (fig. 1.4–3) and differs from the installation described above in the need for an accurate displacement scale, which should be calibrated before the experiment. Furthermore, the torque of the constant speed electric motor is measured, either by an electronic torque meter, or by a kilowatt meter in the electric mains, which has to be calibrated for each electric motor.

The hydrostatic unit delivery passes through a stop valve to the tank and there is a pressure gauge and a relief valve for safety. The experiment consists first in opening the stop valve and measuring the torque absorbed by the hydrostatic unit as a function of the displacement setting. In order to completely eliminate the hydrodynamic losses in the stop valve and piping, it is desirable to remove it from the delivery connection of the hydrostatic unit for the actual run, so that the fluid is returned to the tank without external restriction.

The second part of the experiment is performed by closing the stop valve completely with the displacement set to zero, $\alpha = 0$ then increasing it slowly and measuring the pressure produced and the torque absorbed as a function of α.

This experiment readily allows the determination of the individual loss moments as described in section 1.2. With open port there is no pressure, therefore leakage and dry friction vanish. With zero displacement setting ($\alpha = 0$) the hydrostatic unit absorbs only the

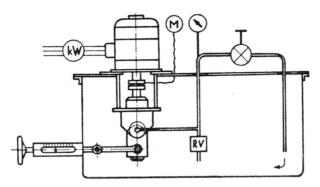

1.4–3 Scheme of open and blocked port test with calibrated displacement scale

viscous friction torque, whilst the torque increase with increasing a corresponds to the hydrodynamic losses.

With blocked port there are no hydrodynamic losses and the small displacement needed to make up for leakage within the unit is the slip displacement defined in equations (1.2–2) and (1.2–18). Measuring the displacement with blocked port gives an accurate indication of the leakage loss and includes the flow effect due to compressibility as treated in section 1.2–d.

The torque with blocked port consists of the slip torque corresponding to slip displacement and pressure, as given by equation (1.2–3) or (1.2–18) together with the dry and viscous friction torques. Deducting from the measured torque the slip torque and the viscous friction obtained with zero displacement and pressure, one obtains the dry friction torque which should be proportional to pressure.

By this method the different torque losses are obtained individually. In practical measurements it is advisable to prepare graphs showing the torque absorbed as a function of a in the open port condition and the torque absorbed and the slip displacement as a function of the pressure produced in the blocked port condition. Examples of these graphs are shown in the figs. 1.4–4 and 1.4–5 respectively. The best possible line is drawn through the experimental points and the loss separation and interpretation is based on these lines. The technique of logarithmic graphs used in experimental physics can be used to represent hydrodynamic and slip torque as straight lines. Without bringing anything fundamentally new they are helpful in interpolating between the measured points as it is simpler to draw a straight line than a curve.

The interpretation of the linear graph of the open port experiment on fig. 1.4–4 is very simple, since the torque absorbed with $a = 0$ is

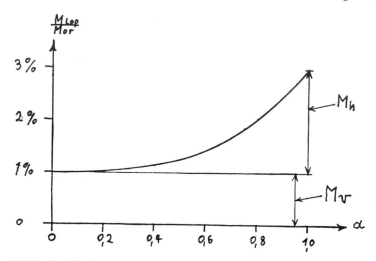

1.4–4 Graph of torque loss against displacement setting in open port
experiment

the viscous friction torque and the increase of absorbed torque with
increasing α is attributable to hydrodynamic loss torque. The interpretation of the graph of the blocked port experiment in fig. 1.4–5 is
as follows. To find the dry friction torque one deducts from the measured torque in the slip torque determined from the slip displacement
α_s read at the same pressure and the viscous friction torque which is
given by the torque measured with zero displacement. Although the
pressure on the graph 1.4–5 is limited to 100 kgf/cm² (1 420 psi) it is
desirable to extend the experiment to as high a pressure as the
hydrostatic unit or the installation will permit.

The advantage of the opened and blocked port experiments is that
they can be performed with a constant speed driving motor with a
power of only a small percentage of that of the hydrostatic unit.
Furthermore since the different torque losses are measured alone, it
is possible to obtain results of high accuracy. Naturally a correction
should be made to allow for the fall of speed of the driving motor
with increasing torque, but this is usually very small.

These experiments are limited by the fact that the loss formulae
1.2–1—1.2–6 are only approximate and that in consequence the loss
coefficients may be slowly variable functions of the operating variables. For example, leakage may increase more than in proportion
to pressure and the hydrodynamic torque loss determined from fig.
1.4–4 may include the viscous friction of the pistons in axial piston
hydrostatic units, which is proportional to the displacement setting.

Nevertheless the experiments are extremely interesting and give useful results.

A variant of the blocked port experiment with full displacement is to load the shaft with a torque, and measure the slip speed and generated pressure as a function of the applied torque. This is more difficult to implement and has the disadvantage that at the very low slip speed both leakage and the dry friction coefficient may have appreciably different values. With variable displacement units the blocked port test as shown in fig. 1.4–3 is always preferable but this variant is needed as part of the open and blocked shaft transmission test to bo described in section 3.4–c.

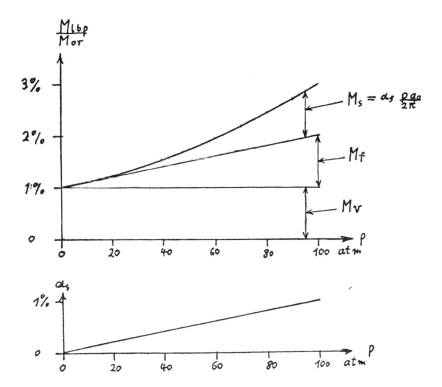

1.4–5 Graph of torque loss and slip displacement against pressure in blocked port experiment

The measurement of torque in the open and blocked port condition suggests an alternative method of (1.2–7 and 1.2–21) of representing the torque loss, to equations. This is possible because only the viscous friction torque loss was measured in both experiments and because the slip torque can be measured separately.

Denoting the measured torque losses by M_{lop} and M_{lbp} and noting that the viscous friction torque is given by the torque loss with $\alpha =$ one obtains

$$M_l = M_{lop} + M_{lbp} - M_{lop}(\alpha = o) - M_s \qquad .. \quad (1.4\text{–}2)$$

The significance of equation 1.4-2 lies in the fact that the loss moment at any pressure and flow is given by the loss moment with flow and zero pressure added to the loss moment without flow and with pressure, together with the correction mentioned.

Similarly the power loss of a hydrostatic unit, given by multiplying the loss moments by the speed and adding the power loss through leakage can be represented as

$$P_l^{(\alpha, p)} = P_{lop} + P_{lbp} - P_{lop}(\alpha = 0) \qquad .. \quad (1.4\text{–}3)$$

Again this signifies that the power loss in a hydrostatic unit including leakage at any flow or, displacement and pressure is given by the power needed to produce the flow at zero pressure plus the power needed to produce pressure without flow, minus the power needed to rotate the unit without flow or pressure. This result is similar to the losses in electric machines, which are given approximately by the sum of current and voltage losses.

CHAPTER 2

POWER TRANSMISSION AND CONTROL

2.1 *Controlled variation of output speed*

In this chapter the operation of a variable speed power transmission will be examined from a general point of view. It will be supposed that the transmission operates from a constant input speed and produces a variable output speed in accordance with some control signals. The following considerations are applicable to all kinds of transmissions.

In order to place the discussion on a definite basis, we will consider the structural diagram shown in fig. 2.1-1. It consists of a prime mover coupled to the input shaft of a variable transmission and the output shaft coupled to the load. The output speed is selected in accordance to the position of the transmission control lever, but the output torque will also have some influence on the speed. The speed of the prime mover is supposed constant, as is approximately the case with an AC induction electric motor or a governed Diesel engine. The case of a variable speed prime mover will be treated in section 4.3.

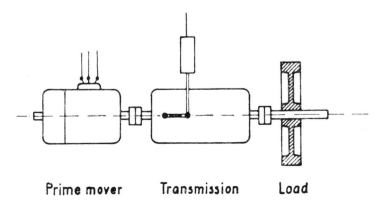

Prime mover   Transmission   Load

2.1-1 Schematic arrangement or structural diagram of hydrostatic transmission

For a description of the operation of the structural diagram in fig. 2.1–1 refer to fig. 2.1–2, which represents a similar functional diagram.

The properties of and the relations between the structural and functional diagrams are treated in Appendix A2.

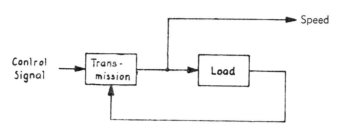

2.1-2 Functional diagram of hydrostatic transmission

In fig. 2.1–2 the position of the transmission control lever or, in general terms, the control signal, causes the transmission to produce the desired output speed. This speed produces an opposing torque depending on the characteristics of the load. The torque has some influence on the output shaft speed of the transmission with a given control signal, as indicated by the feedback connection on fig. 2.1–2, although with hydrostatic transmissions the influence is small. This feedback is not a physical connection, but is caused by the torque acting on the output shaft and so the transmission.

The torque on the output shaft is caused by the load as it responds to the control signal. It may vary due to disturbances at the load and depend on the acceleration due to the control signal. Consequently the torque is momentarily independent of the speed. A familiar example is the motor car where the speed is selected by the driver, and opposing torque at a given speed depends on the characteristics of the car, on the acceleration desired and on disturbances caused by variable gradients and road surfaces. For satisfactory operation of most transmissions it is necessary that the control signal either automatic or human, does not command speeds or accelerations beyond the safe limits.

Although the above functional diagram is useful for adapting hydrostatic transmission to a load, an alternative but equivalent functional diagram as shown in fig. 2.1–3 is frequently used. In this diagram the transmission produces torque in accordance with the control signal. This torque produces a speed, which depending on the load influences the torque produced by the transmission through the feedback connection shown in fig. 2.1–3. In other words, in this functional representation, torque is developed at each speed in accordance with the control setting. Generally, the functional diagram of fig. 2.1–2, where a speed is selected and the opposing torque constitutes a response of the load is more useful where the speed is

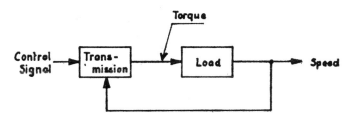

2.1-3 Alternative functional diagram of hydrostatic transmission

nearly independent of the torque as in hydrostatic transmissions. Conversely the functional diagram (fig. 2.1–3), where the torque is fixed and speed produces the feedback signal, is preferable where the torque produced is nearly independent of speed, as in a friction coupling.

2.2 Torque multiplication and "apparent power"

A convenient representation of the operation of a variable transmission is a graph relating output torque and speed (fig. 2.2–1). It shows the possible output torque and speed of an ideal, loss-free transmission having a certain input power limit. Maximum torque is developed at zero output speed or stalled output shaft and at very low speeds up to the speed n_{2dir}. At higher output speeds less torque can be developed due to the horse power limitation until a maximum output speed n_{2max} the torque becomes M_{2dir}. Since losses are neglected here, the power available on the output shaft between n_{2dir} and n_{2max} is equal to the input power.

$$P_i = 2\pi\, M_{2max}\, n_{2dir} = 2\pi\, M_{2dir}\, n_{2max} \qquad .. \quad (2.2\text{--}1)$$

Characteristic of the drive requirements are the maximum torque and maximum speed, because the transmission will be required to handle both at different times. Thus both transmission and output shaft must be able to withstand the highest torque and the maximum speed.

Sometimes it is an advantage to be able to combine both maximum output torque and maximum output speed available at different times. This is called "apparent power", in analogy to electrical engineering, and given by

$$P_{ap} = 2\pi \, M_{2max} \cdot N_{2max} \qquad \qquad .. \quad (2.2.-2)$$

The advantage of the use of the apparent power is that it is independent of any final reduction between transmission and load.

It should be noted, that the characteristics of fig. 2.2–1 show only the maximum torque that can be developed as a function of speed. In practice, as in motor cars, the actual torque will be often smaller in accordance with control signals.

It is of interest also to consider the power relationships of an ideal transmission, as represented on fig. 2.2–2. It shows the available output power as a function of output speed. This power is necessarily

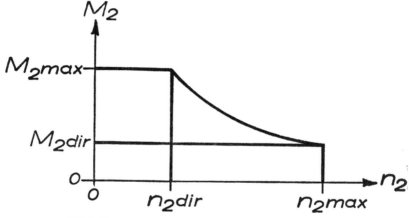

2.2–1 Output torque-speed graph of ideal transmission

zero at stalled output shaft and increases linearly with output speed, until at n_{2dir} the full power of the prime mover is available. With higher output speed the power available remains constant corresponding to the drop in available torque on fig. 2.2–1 between n_{2dir} and n_{2max}. In the graph of fig. 2.2–2 the apparent power is obtained by continuing the initial linear power increase until the maximum output speed n_{2max}. Thus this figure shows very clearly the relation between the power of the prime mover and apparent power.

Since the full torque of the prime mover must be produced at maximum output speed the full power is developed. At low output

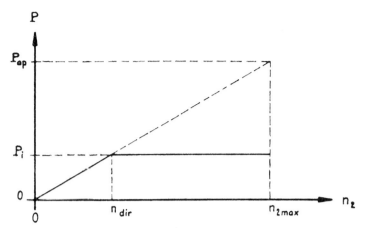

2.2-2 Graph of output power against speed of ideal transmission showing apparent power

speeds, the higher torque developed on the output shaft must be produced within the transmission. This is represented quantitatively by the torque multiplication factor defined by:

$$\gamma = \frac{M_{2max}}{M_{2dir}} \qquad \qquad .. \quad (2.2\text{-}3)$$

by combining equations (2.2–1, 2 and 3) one obtains

$$P_{ap} = \gamma \, P_i \qquad \qquad .. \quad (2.2\text{-}4)$$

Equation (2.2–4) shows that the apparent power is given by the power of the prime mover multiplied by the torque multiplication. Therefore torque multiplication is a significant factor of the performance of a transmission.

2.3 Clutches or Couplings

The operation of clutches will now be described as an application of the ideas introduced in the preceding sections.

A clutch is the simplest variable speed transmission, where the full output speed is equal to the input speed and is obtained by fastening or fully engaging the clutch and lower output speeds by continuous sliding. Obviously the clutches must be able to withstand continuous sliding, but this does not influence the fundamental behaviour.

The highest output torque, equal to torque of the prime mover or input torque is available at the maximum output speed n_{2max}, and the available output torque cannot increase at lower speeds. Therefore no torque is produced in the clutch, or the torque multiplication is equal to 1. The very simple torque speed relation of a clutch is shown by the solid line in fig. 2.3–1.

The full output power is available only at maximum output speed, and this power decreases linearly with decreasing speed. Neglecting the very small torque loss, efficiency is equal to unity at n_{2max}, and decreases linearly with n_2 as shown by the dotted line in fig. 2.3–1.

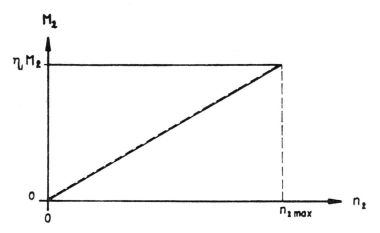

2.3–1 Graph of output torque (solid line) and efficiency (dotted line) against clutch speed

2.4 *Clutch with changeable gearbox*

As a second example we discuss a transmission consisting of a clutch with a motor car type speed gear box. Taking for simplicity a three-speed gear box, its operation can be described by assuming that a simple clutch is driving through the top gear, in accordance with the treatment in the preceding section. To avoid a large loss of power and to give more torque at low speed a lower (second) gear ratio is added. This produces, in conjunction with the coupling a lower speed and higher torque. Finally a bottom gear is provided, that again behaves like a simple clutch but having a still lower speed and higher torque. The torque curve is shown in fig. 2.4–1, where the high torque at low speed can be seen and the power in fig. 2.4–2. Full power can be developed at the output shaft at the highest of all the three gear ratios.

The transmission consisting of a gear box and a clutch has a torque multiplication equal to the ratio of the top to the bottom gear, and also the apparent power is increased by the torque multiplication factor. Compared to the single clutch, the amount of slip and energy loss is greatly reduced and there are now three values of output speed without slip with constant input speed. There is nothing fundamental to prevent to use more gear ratios, in order to space points without

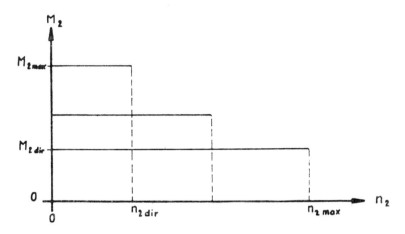

2.4-1 Graph of output torque against speed of 3 speed gearbox

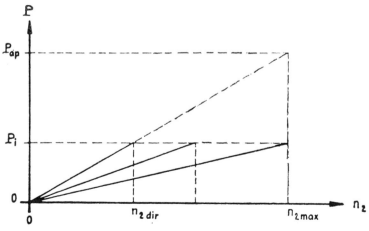

2.4-2 Graph of output power against speed of 3 speed gearbox

slip more nearly together, and in fact, small motor cars and heavy vehicles have 4 or 6 gears.

Since automotive couplings or friction clutches are not suitable for continuous slipping the final selection of speed is done by variation of the engine speed, and motor car engines are designed to have a large usable engine speed range.

⌈Instead of the clutch it is possible to use a hydrostatic transmission, working together with a change speed gear box, to give a very large speed range. This is further treated in section 5.1.⌉

A practical limitation in the use of clutches with gear boxes is the time required and the skill necessary for shifting the gears.

2.5 *Very slow speed performance*

Another important factor in the operation of a variable transmission is the performance at stalled or very slowly revolving output shaft. Necessarily any load must be accelerated by applying torque from the stalled condition and in some cases it is desirable to maintain the output shaft stationary by the transmission despite external torque without friction brakes.

With stalled output shaft, no power is supplied to the load, therefore the efficiency is zero. However, the power required by the transmission to produce a certain torque on a stalled output shaft is of considerable practical importance, and in this section this operation is described quantitatively, by introducing a suitable new parameter.

The new parameter should indicate the power required by the transmission to produce the output torque with stalled output shaft, yet has to be independent of final gear reduction between transmission and load. Therefore the output torque is multiplied by the maximum output speed and divided by input power to yield the desired parameter indicating torque multiplication at stalled output shaft.

$$\gamma_s = \frac{M_2 \cdot N_{2max}}{M_1 \cdot n_1} \qquad \cdot\cdot \quad (2.5\text{--}5)$$

This parameter is independent of any final reduction between transmission and load, because such reduction would increase output torque and reduce output speed by the same factor.

It is interesting to discuss the stalled torque multiplication of a simple clutch. With a stalled output shaft, slipping clutch and a prime mover running at maximum speed, the developed torque is equal to engine torque. Therefore the stalled torque multiplication is equal to 1, that is no torque multiplication within the clutch.

As next example consider a transmission consisting of a clutch with change speed gear box where the top ratio is direct drive as described in the preceding section. Here the torque is increased by the gear ratio, while maximum output speed in top gear remains equal to input speed. The highest torque increase is given by the lowest gear ratio and therefore torque multiplication at stalled output shaft is also equal to the ratio of top to lowest gear. Usual values in European motor cars are $\gamma_s = 3......4$.

In both these examples, normal torque multiplication and torque multiplication at stall (γ_s and γ) are equal. This is the case only when the full torque of a prime mover is required to produce full output torque at stall.

In Ward-Leonard electric transmissions and hydrostatic transmissions the input power needed to produce high output torque without speed is quite small. Particularly in a hydrostatic transmission, where input power has only to make up for the leakage and dry friction of both units and viscous friction in the primary. Flow losses are zero because there is only leakage flow. This will be further discussed in section 3.4c but here it should be mentioned that normal torque multiplication in hydrostatic transmission is usually limited to three or four ($\gamma = 3,4$) but torque multiplication at stall is about ($\gamma_s = 25......40$). In other words to produce maximum output torque, the hydrostatic transmission needs only a 1/40th of the power corresponding to this torque multiplied by maximum output speed.

For completeness it should be mentioned that in hydrokinetic transmissions, where the full engine power is needed to produce full torque at stalled output shaft, γ and γ_s are equal and usually around 5 or 6.

2.6 *Reversing and braking of output shaft*

The treatment of the operation of a variable speed power transmission in this chapter has so far only been concerned with driving a load; with the transmission imparting a positive torque and speed to the output shaft. It is a great advantage that a hydrostatic transmission is able not only to drive the output shaft in the reverse sense, but also to brake it both when rotating forward and in reverse. This means that the hydrostatic transmission can exercise a negative torque with positive speed, brake the output shaft in the normal direction of rotation, produce negative torque and negative speed corresponding to reverse rotation, and finally positive torque with negative speed, corresponding to reverse braking.

In consequence the graph relating output torque and speed has
to be enlarged to give negative values both of torque and speed, as
represented on fig. 2.6–1. The limits on torque and rotative speed
are as before and have the same absolute values. If the losses in
the transmission are neglected, the power limits are the same as
before with the graph showing only positive values of torque and
speed.

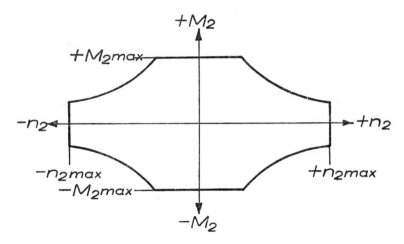

2.6–1 Graph of output torque against speed admitting negative torques and
speeds

Only with forward and reverse driving does the hydrostatic transmission draw power from the prime mover, when braking it returns
power to the primary shaft, that is it drives it in the primary direction of rotation. In this state the secondary is pumping and primary is motoring, and power travels from the load back to the prime
mover. The losses which are inseparable from flow, are now deducted
from the power appearing at the primary shaft. Ignoring the losses,
the magnitude of the torque and speed returned to the primary
shaft is the same when braking as when driving, but the sense of the
torque is reversed.

Within the limits shown on fig. 2.6–1, both secondary torque and
speed can vary freely, and the relationship between them is a property of the load, depending to the required acceleration and disturbing influences. For a normal motor car, the disturbing influences
are the gradients and any variation of rolling resistance. In a motor
car equipped with a manually controlled hydrostatic transmission,
torque reverses instantly on taking the foot off the accelerator, since

the car is then driving the engine, and the speed changes slowly due to the inertia of the car. In fig. 2.6–1 the power limit is shown equal for both driving and braking, which implies that the absorption capacity of the prime mover is equal to its power production capacity. With AC induction electric motors this is the case whilst they are connected to the electric mains, but internal combustion engines can absorb only a small fraction of their rated power. In order to allow braking with a hydrostatic transmission driven by an internal combustion engine, exhaust brakes are available on some engines, or otherwise a special hydraulic energy dissipator as described in Section 4.5 can be fitted.

CHAPTER 3

PROPERTIES OF HYDROSTATIC TRANSMISSION

After the treatment of hydrostatic units in chapter 1 and of the general properties of variable speed transmission in chapter 2, the object of this chapter is to describe how to combine hydrostatic units and circuits in order to make a variable hydrostatic transmission, and to consider the quantitative aspects of adapting a given size of hydrostatic transmission to the driven load.

3.1 *Selection of hydrostatic circuits*

In the present section the properties of circuits, hydrostatic units and their accessories will be discussed together with some remarks on the flexibility of characteristics and installation. A study of these relationships is of importance in order to select the best possible hydrostatic circuit and transmission for the contemplated application.

a) *Constant displacement primary and secondary*

The simplest possible arrangement for the hydrostatic transmission of power has a fixed displacement primary unit pumping oil from a reservoir to a fixed displacement secondary unit. This is shown schematically in fig. 3.1–1, where the primary unit is mounted in a large tank, while the secondary may be located at a distance and connected to the tank only by the delivery return lines. To obtain variable output speed, a controllable bypass valve is provided, which returns fluid directly from the delivery line into the tank. Thus the secondary speed is reduced by the volume of flow through the bypass valve.

It is expedient to suppose for the moment that the displacements of the primary and secondary hydrostatic units are equal. The highest output speed is equal to the input speed and is obtained by closing the bypass valve—neglecting leakage. Discounting the small torque loss, the maximum output torque is equal to the torque available from the prime mover at the primary shaft.

Lower output speeds are simply obtained by controlled opening of the bypass valve, which diverts a part of the flow from the secondary. Naturally there is an energy loss equal to the flow through the bypass valve multiplied by the delivery pressure. The flow through this valve corresponds to the slip speed, that is, the difference between the output and the input speed. It should be noted that reducing the output speed does not produce a higher torque at the secondary shaft, the highest output torque being at most equal to the torque of the prime mover. In other words the simple hydrostatic arrangement comprising a primary and secondary of constant displacement behaves exactly like a clutch, as treated in detail in

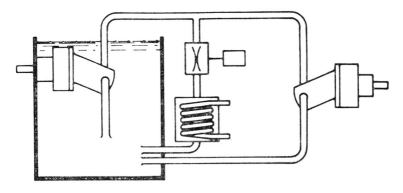

3.1-1 Scheme of transmission with two fixed displacement units and speed control by bypass

section 2.3. In particular the fig. 2.3–1 represents very closely the operation of this simple driving arrangement. The difference from an ordinary friction clutch is that in the hydrostatic arrangement some torque loss, due to dry friction, viscous friction and hydrodynamical losses in both hydrostatic units will always be present, usually larger than the very low torque loss in friction clutches or hydrokinetic couplings. Furthermore, the leakage flow always involves a very small slip or speed difference between primary and secondary shaft, even if the bypass valve is completely closed. It is an advantage of the hydrostatic arrangement, compared to friction clutches, that the heat corresponding to the energy loss is not produced at the friction faces with the consequent dissipation problems. Instead the heat is produced in the bypass valve and mainly appears as an increase of the temperature of the fluid leaving that valve. It is easy, of course to send the output of the bypass valve through a cooler, as indicated in fig. 3.1–1 and so maintain temperature of the fluid within admissible limits.

Little is changed in the performance of the constant displacement hydrostatic transmission, if the primary and secondary units of different displacements are taken. In some cases a secondary of double displacement is used reducing the output shaft speed by one half and doubling the output torque, as a fixed reduction gear would do. The only difference is that the leakage flow of the double displacement secondary would also be doubled, according to equation (1.2–1). This is true if the leakage coefficient remains constant, or nearly so, as would be expected from the discussion in section 1.3c on model laws.

For proper operation it is necessary to maintain the oil level above the intake, to avoid drawing in air. It is also necessary to prevent reversal of the output torque either by arrangement of the controls or of the machine being driven, as this would cause cavitation in the delivery line and severe vibrations with the danger of overloading all components.

Another important characteristic of the constant displacement hydrostatic transmission is that the speed ratio depends very much on the secondary torque. This is best explained by reference to the functional diagram shown in fig. 3.1–2.

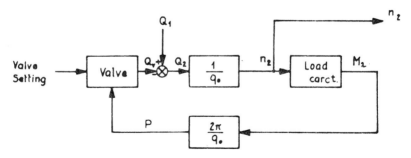

3.1–2 Functional diagram of transmission with two fixed displacement unit and speed control by bypass

In this diagram 3.1–2 the valve setting is the control signal which determines the flow through the bypass valve which is deducted from the primary flow to give the secondary flow. The flow entering the secondary produces an output speed depending on its displacement. The output speed produces an opposing torque in accordance with the load characteristics, and this produces the delivery pressure as given by the fundamental equations 1.1–1 and 1.1–2.

The speed ratio is dependent on the output torque, because flow through the bypass valve with a given valve setting is dependent on the pressure applied. This is represented on the functional diagram of fig. 3.1–2 by the line and arrow entering the box representing the valve. The magnitude of this effect depends on the pressure flow/pressure characteristics of the valve but for normal turbulent flow conditions in the valve an increase of 10% in the load torque would result in a reduction of 5% in the output speed. Obviously it is quite possible to use commercial pressure compensated flow control valves, which are nearly independent of pressure and sometimes also thermostatically compensated to reduce the dependence of the secondary speed on secondary torque.

Since the constant displacement hydrostatic transmissions have only the same performance as a clutch, there is not much to commend it for any application except that it can be used for hydrostatic transport of power by pipes over moderate distances. It may, however, be used for its simplicity, especially if the setting of the bypass valve can be automatically controlled as in the fan drives described in section 6.2.

3.1 b) *Variable primary with fixed secondary*

The hydrostatic transmission incorporating a variable primary and a constant displacement secondary is the basic and most widely used form of hydrostatic power transmission. This may be because for most applications it unites all advantages of performance and still has reasonable simplicity. Hydraulically there are two possible circuits, the open and closed circuit, which will now be described.

A typical open circuit hydrostatic transmission is shown schematically in fig. 3.1–3, where a variable primary unit is mounted inside a large tank. It is usual to submerge the pump well below the surface of the oil. It is also possible for the pump to be above the oil level, but the fluid surface must not pass through the pump itself or the oil may be churned up by the moving parts of the unit and aerate. The oil passed from the pipe (a) to an externally mounted secondary unit, the oil returning through the pipe (b) to the main oil tank. The leakage of the secondary can be taken by the return line. For protection against overload, a relief valve is shown on connecting pipes (a) and (b).

The same hydraulic circuit was shown in figure I–1, variable secondary speed being produced by variation of flow. With constant input speed n_1, the flow is determined by the variable displacement setting α which must be controlled according to the requirements of the driven machine. This control is represented symbolically in fig. 3.1–3 by a hand wheel and travelling nut. Although the flow varies with displacement setting it is almost unaffected by the pressure. Therefore this is a constant-flow system with variable pressure as long as displacement setting is held constant.

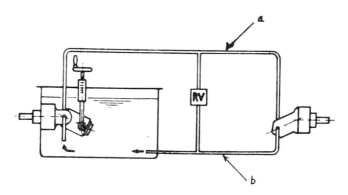

3.1–3 Scheme of variable primary transmission with open circuit

The simple open circuit hydrostatic transmission has two limitations:

1) Neither torque reversal in the secondary shaft nor braking torque on the output is possible. The control arrangements must ensure that this condition is avoided, as it would lead to cavitation in the delivery line and possible overload and damage to the units.

2) Cavitation may occur in the inlet pipe of the pumping unit due to high flow velocity. In consequent the maximum speed of this simple transmission is limited.

The onset of cavitation in the inlet line depends on the absolute pressure in it, and this is the reason why the primary is usually submerged. Cavitation can be delayed by submerging the primary deeper, if the general layout permits. In essence it can be said that the inlet or priming pressure is produced by the depth of submersion and the atmospheric pressure of the air.

The closed circuit is more complicated and has more components, but it is frequently used because it allows the reversal of the secondary torque. This is necessary not only in order to brake the driven machine but also for driving it in reverse.

The general arrangement of a closed circuit hydrostatic transmission with variable primary is represented schematically in fig.

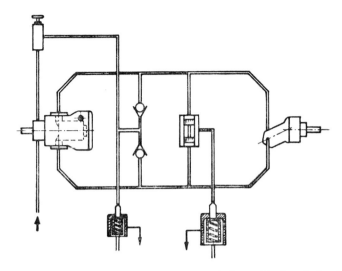

3.1-4 Scheme of variable primary transmission with closed circuit

3.1–4 and as a hydraulic diagram in fig. 3.1–5. Whilst with the open circuit the return oil had to travel through the tank, now there are two main lines (a) and (b) which carry the oil from the primary to the secondary. It is normal to supercharge this circuit by the use of a priming pump, preferably mounted in the casing of the primary

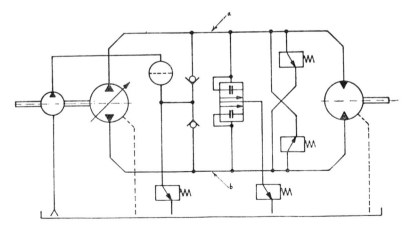

3.1-5 Hydraulic circuit of variable primary transmission with closed circuit

hydrostatic unit. It draws fluid from a tank, passes it through the filter and delivers it through a non-return valve into the main line which is at the lower pressure. The special relief valve shown limits the priming pressure to a desirable value, which depends on the application, ranging from 2–3 kgf/cm² (30–50 psi) for normal speeds to 8–10 kgf/cm² (120–150 psi) for the highest speeds used on vehicles. The two non-return valves in fig. 3.1–4 and 3.1–5 prevent cavitation in either of the main lines and thus act in a similar way to the free surface of the open circuit. The valves can also be connected directly to an oil tank as is sometimes done in low speed transmissions, but usually it is preferable to supercharge them by the use of a priming pump with filter and relief valve.

As a further refinement of the closed circuit a decompression valve* is shown in figs. 3.1–4 and 3.1–5. This valve vents whichever of the main lines is at low pressure and some oil escapes at priming pressure and so that the energy loss is very low. A relief valve is normally incorporated in the decompression valve, as shown in the diagrams in order to maintain a definite priming pressure in the main lines. The decompression valve is also needed to expel the air from the system on starting after a long rest.

The reason for bleeding off a certain quantity of hydraulic fluid is first to be cooled and filtered. Both are very necessary for high speed installations. A practical design of a decompression valve comprises two mushroom valves, with mating conical seats, not un-like i.c. engine valves, disposed in such a way that both stems touch. Thus one mushroom valve is always kept closed by the high pressure on one side and its stem forces the other mushroom valve open against priming pressure. It is also possible to use spool valves, with the pressure acting on the end faces, but the mushroom valve has the advantage of sealing perfectly in its conical seat at very high pressure.

The capacity of the priming pump in a closed circuit must be sufficient to replace the leakage of the main hydrostatic units at the highest system pressure and temperature and provide some flow through the decompression valve. It thus depends on the design of the hydrostatic units, but normally it is selected as 10 or 15% of the maximum system flow as the priming pressure is low in com-parison with the delivery pressure in normal operation, the energy loss of the priming pump is negligible in practice.

Since now both main lines can be under delivery pressure it is necessary to fit a relief valve to each. In order to prevent collapse

---

* Also called by some a venting valve or shuttle valve.

of priming pressure of the priming pump capacity is insufficient when the relief valve is blowing continuously it is recommended that the relief valves discharge to the other main line and not to the tank as shown in fig. 3.1–5.

The importance of using a closed circuit is that the secondary shaft can be reversed or braked. In all machines where this is required, as in vehicle drives the closed circuit is an absolute necessity.

While the priming pressure is needed to prevent cavitation, it should not be too high, because of the energy consumption and pressure loads it produces within the hydrostatic unit which do not produce useful torque.

For a study of the influence of the priming pressure on the actual pressure within the main system we refer to fig. 3.1–6. Where the abscissa represents the output torque, the positive ordinate the pressure p_a in the main line (a) and the negative ordinate the pressure p_b in the main line (b). The form of both pressure curves p_a and p_b shows the action of the non-return valve very well admitting priming fluid and maintaining the pressure in the corresponding main line at least equal to the priming pressure.

As it was mentioned in section 1.2, with pressure in both main lines, the torque of a hydrostatic unit is given by the difference of the absolute pressures in the lines. In other words the torque of the unit is given by the fundamental equation 1.1–2, inserting as the acting pressure p_{ac} the difference of absolute pressures in both main lines. In fig. 3.1–6 the acting pressure p_{ac} is obtained by graphic addition of the pressures in both main lines. As it is seen, it is strictly proportional to the output torque (neglecting torque losses), and both the output torque and the pressure can assume negative values. This is possible because the acting pressure is really the difference between two real pressures, and negative real pressures or cavitation in the main line is prevented by the non-return valves admitting priming fluid where needed.

Some remarks on the effect of priming pressure on leakage may be appropriate. Strictly speaking, as it was defined in section 1.2–1 leakage is proportional to the real pressure existing in one main line. Some flow is lost from the system and is mostly returned to the tank as external leakage, while some small part may find its way into the other main line as internal leakage. The priming pressure in the other main line produces further leakage most of which goes to the tank.

Whilst leakage is subtracted from the flow in the pressure line and most of it returns to the tank.

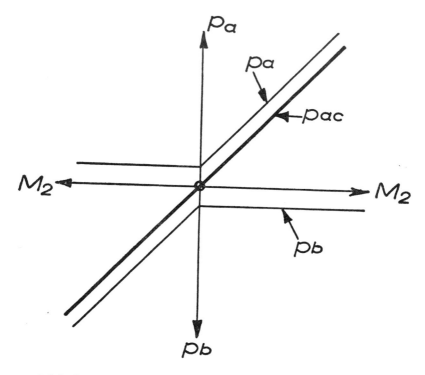

3.1–6 Graph of pressure in conduits (a) and (b) against output torque

It is normal to neglect the influence of priming pressure on leakage, since priming pressure is small compared to the usual operating pressures and one is mostly interested in the amount of leakage at the higher part of the range of operating pressures. Assuming this, the leakage flow is proportional to the acting pressure as defined above and can become positive or negative depending on the sign of the acting pressure. Negative leakage thus means a flow leaving the main line (b) and manifesting itself as a speed reduction at the output shaft negative. This property is used in section 3.3 for the mathematical treatment of hydrostatic transmission.

The flow produced in a hydrostatic transmission with a variable displacement primary rotating with constant speed is very nearly proportional to the displacement setting a. Thus also the secondary speed is proportional to the displacement setting except for the small effect of leakage, as will be treated more in detail in section 3.3.

c) *Variable primary and variable secondary*

While so far hydrostatic transmissions with variable primary and constant displacement secondary have been considered, there is no fundamental reason against also making the secondary with variable displacement. This can be done either with the open circuit shown in fig. 3.1–3 or the closed circuit of fig. 3.1–4. Contrary to the constant displacement secondary where the output shaft speed is proportional to the flow in the main system, reducing secondary displacement increases shaft speed and reduces torque for the same flow and main pressure. Thus the performances of a hydrostatic transmission with variable displacement of the primary and variable displacement of the secondary is given by the following two equations

$$n_2 = n_1 \frac{a_1}{a_2} \qquad \qquad .. \quad (3.1\text{--}1)$$

$$M_2 = M_1 \frac{a_2}{a_1} \qquad \qquad .. \quad (3.1\text{--}2)$$

a_1 = primary displacement

a_2 = secondary displacement

Equations 3.1–1 and 3.1–2 are the generalization of the equations I-1 and I-2 given in the introduction. Since the output speed can now be increased indefinitely by reducing secondary displacement a_2, the transmission control must avoid too small a secondary displacement which would result in speeds beyond the safe limit and consequent damage. Furthermore, if the controller should reduce secondary displacement to zero no flow except leakage flow can be accepted by the secondary and the relief valve will blow. Actually, because of friction effects, the secondary may become self-locking at some low displacement.

A general disadvantage of the variable secondary is its more complicated mechanism which is of special importance when the secondary is mounted near to the driven machine, whilst the prime mover with primary and the valve gear can be mounted in one casing at a convenient place.

d) *Constant pressure variable displacement secondary*

The danger of blocked flow with variable displacement secondaries as treated in the preceding part of this section, comes essentially from the fact that a hydrostatic primary unit driven with constant shaft speed and with the displacement controlled externally is actually a controlled flow installation. In effect, the flow with given primary displacement and speed varies very little with pressure, and when the secondary cannot accept flow because of reduced or zero displacement, the primary flow is maintained by a relief valve opening. Without a relief valve some part of the transmission will break down.

Quite different characteristics are obtained when a variable secondary is fed from a constant pressure source instead of a constant flow source. This constant pressure source consists, preferably, of a variable displacement hydrostatic unit, as represented in fig. 3.1–7. Here the hydrostatic unit is suspended vertically from an electric motor into a tank, and is equipped with a constant pressure controller

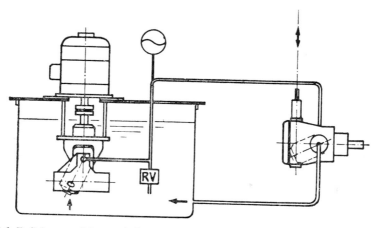

3.1–7 Scheme of transmission with constant pressure source and variable secondary in open circuit

which reduces displacement as soon as the calibrated pressure is reached, and effectively maintains constant pressure despite variations. It is desirable to incorporate the relief valve and accumulator shown, as protection against pressure surges.

The left side of fig. 3.1–7 thus effectively constitutes a hydraulic generator, which delivers constant pressure to a variable displacement secondary on the right side of the figure. The flow leaving from the secondary returns to the tank through the other main line. In essence one has here a hydrostatic transmission with both variable primary and variable secondary, where the primary displacement is controlled automatically in order to maintain a constant pressure.

The constant pressure variable secondary transmission can also be used in a closed circuit, as represented in the circuit diagram in fig. 3.1–8. Since pressure acts always on one side, the valves required are much simpler than the ones in the closed circuits of fig. 3.1–4. The priming pump takes fluid from the reservoir and forces it through a filter into the main line (b), which is always at priming pressure.

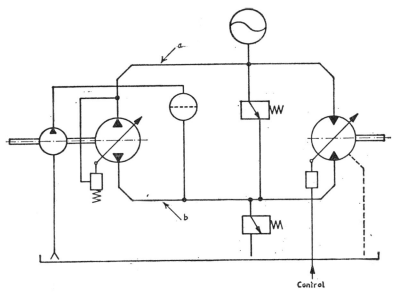

3.1–8 Circuit of transmission with constant pressure source and variable secondary in closed circuit

There is no non-return feeding valve or decompression valve and it is possible to use only one priming pressure relief valve connected to the main line (b), as shown in fig. 3.1–8 which also shows the accumulator and the single main pressure relief valve now needed.

From a control point of view, we have constant pressure, and the flow is determined by the shaft speed and the displacement of the secondary.

For controlling the shaft speed of the secondary, it is important to note that as the pressure is constant the secondary shaft torque is proportional to the displacement setting, if losses are neglected. By reversing secondary displacement, braking and reversing of the load

6

is also possible with this simple open circuit. Whilst the detail control characteristics will be treated in section 3.3, it should be mentioned here that there is nothing to prevent the secondary shaft running away or overspeeding and thus the controller must take into account the secondary speed limit.

An important advantage of the constant pressure variable secondary hydrostatic transmission is that in consequence of the constant system pressure, it is possible to feed several secondaries from one primary or one hydraulic generator, and to control each secondary independently. For this purpose either the open circuit of fig. 3.1–7 or the closed circuit of fig. 3.1–8 remains unchanged except that there would be two or several secondaries each with its own controller. Naturally it is necessary to install a primary hydrostatic unit with sufficient flow capacity. Furthermore it is quite possible to drive other accessories such as distributor valves, rams etc. without disturbing the control characteristics. This latter property is of special value in larger installations when several secondaries and accessories are fed from one hydrostatic primary unit. If the drive characteristics are such that it is not necessary to operate all secondaries with full power at the same time, primary and prime mover can be made smaller with consequent economy.

Summarizing the constant-pressure variable displacement secondary unit hydrostatic transmission has many advantages and would merit more frequent use. Perhaps a disadvantage is that the full system pressure is always acting on all hydrostatic units.

e) *Circuits for multiple primaries and secondaries*

In this part, the combination of several primaries with several secondaries will be discussed. Some times it is desirable in hydrostatic transmission to use not one, but several primaries and secondaries, not only because of commercially available sizes but also for convenience of control and installation.

Probably the most useful combination comprises one variable primary feeding to constant displacement secondaries hydraulically in parallel as shown in fig. 3.1–9. There is equal pressure on both secondaries, which will therefore produce the same torque and with the parallel circuit the sum of the flows of the secondaries is equal to the primary flow. Given these conditions the flow to each secondary can vary freely, whilst the torque remains equal so that there is complete differential action between both secondaries. This is sometimes useful especially with vehicles drives, but reduction gears between secondaries and wheels will usually be required.

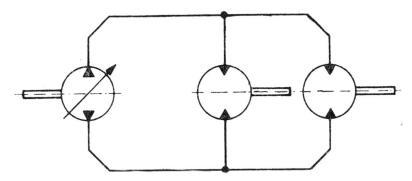

3.1-9 Circuit with variable primary and two constant secondaries in parallel

In a hydrostatic transmission with two secondaries, each with a displacement equal to the maximum displacement of the variable primary, the highest secondary speed is one half the primary speed, and the highest secondary torque is equal to double of the primary torque at full displacement and correspondingly more at lower displacement. Thus this arrangement has a built in reduction ratio of 1:2. Other ranges of output speeds can of course be obtained by using secondaries with different displacements.

A disadvantage of the hydrostatic transmission involving two secondaries and one primary of equal maximum displacement, is that the torque or speed capabilities of all of them cannot be fully used. In effect, with parallel secondaries, the highest secondary speed is one half primary speed. If the speed of the primary is chosen near its limit so as to give maximum power generation, the maximum speed of the secondaries is only half their limiting speed, which means that they cannot work at full power.

For completeness another possible circuit should be mentioned for two secondaries hydraulically in series, as shown in fig. 3.1–10 where the flow through both secondaries is equal, so giving equal shaft speeds. Furthermore the sum of the pressures across both secondaries is equal to the pressure across the primary. Thus it can be said that the pressures build up across each secondary as is necessary to maintain equal shaft speeds, and combine to oppose the flow leaving the primary.

A serious disadvantage affects transmission with secondaries in series (fig. 3.1–10). Here the pressure on the primary is equal the sum of the pressures across the secondaries. When the primary pressure is chosen according to the pressure limit of the unit, the pressure across each secondary is one half this value if they have both to supply

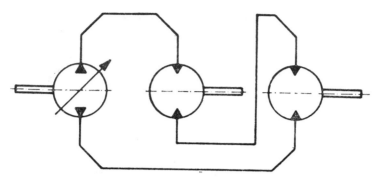

3.1-10 Circuit with variable primary and two constant secondaries in series

equal torque. Thus this circuit does not allow the secondaries to be used to the limit of their torque capacity. Furthermore the secondary on the upstream side has a considerable proportion of the total pressure at its outlet port with consequent loads on some internal parts such as the returning pistons in axial piston pumps. This causes overloading and difficulties with shaft seals, unless special designs are used. The circuit with two secondaries in series would seem therefore to be only rarely practicable.

Another possible hydrostatic transmission circuit employs two primaries both connected in parallel and one secondary (fig. 3.1-11). In this example only one primary is variable, the other one being of the constant displacement type.

This circuit has interesting control properties. As the highest output speed is double the input speed which is obtained by setting the variable primary fully forward. Output speed equal to input speed is obtained by setting the primary to zero and at fully reversed primary $a_1 = -1$, zero output speed is obtained. In the lower half of the output speed range, where the variable primary is reversed and a_1 is negative, it is really motoring, giving torque back to the common input shaft. This has no particular disadvantage, but the flow losses are high when one unit is motoring. Nevertheless, the other losses are unaffected and equal to the losses that would be obtained by using a variable primary of double capacity. Naturally, it is not possible to reverse the speed of the output shaft with this circuit, unless the variable primary is larger than the constant one.

A slight disadvantage of using two primaries and a secondary of identical size in parallel is that the maximum speeds of the units are different, with consequent incomplete use of the speed limits as mentioned above. This can of course be circumvented either by using two secondaries in parallel, or one secondary of larger size.

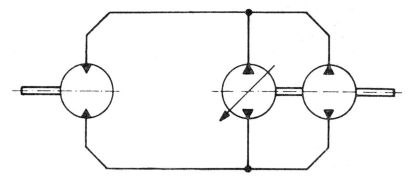

3.1–11 Circuit with one variable and one constant primary in parallel with one constant secondary

A hydrostatic transmission incorporating one constant displacement and one variable displacement primary together with one or two secondaries is sometimes used where reverse output shaft speed is not required. This depends to a certain extent on the available sizes of hydrostatic units and on the particular situation.

3.2 Selection of hydrostatic transmission ratings

a) *Variable primary and constant secondary*

In this section the quantitative aspects of fitting hydrostatic transmission to a machine will be discussed. This is the most important step, in selecting a suitable transmission for the requirements of the particular drive after the hydraulic circuit has been decided upon.

The driven machine or load is best specified by a graph giving its torque and speed. As pointed out before, for a given speed the torque drawn by the load may vary because of acceleration or because of disturbances on the load, so that momentarily the torque may be independent of the load speed. Nevertheless, it will be possible to establish an upper limit for the torque required by the load and also an upper limit for the required speed. This can be entered into a torque speed graph of the load, such as fig. 3.2–1.

It is useful to call a particular combination of torque and speed the "driving state", which is then represented by a point in the torque/speed graph of the load. The independence of torque and speed implies that the point representing the driving state can take any position within the torque and speed limits of the graph.

The torque/speed graph of the load (fig. 3.2–1) is the starting point for a quantitative determination of a suitable secondary. It is necessary to mark on the graph the highest necessary torque M_{2max} and the highest required speed n_{2max}. Both values enclose a rectangle (fig. 3.2–1), the corner of which represents the apparent power which is defined in equation 2.2–1 as the product of maximum torque and maximum speed.

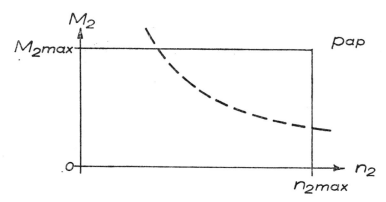

3.2–1 Load-torque-speed graph for selecting secondary ratings

It is easy to obtain from the graph of load torques and speeds the traction force and linear speed of a vehicle or winch.

The rectangle shown in heavy lines in fig. 3.2–1 with the apparent power at the apex represents all possible driving states that can be realized within the speed and torque limits. Braking the output shaft, that is exercising a negative torque on it, and driving or braking in reverse are mentioned briefly in section 3.3.

In many cases it is desirable to introduce a further limit on the possible driving states by a power limit as shown in fig. 3.2–1 by the dotted line. There is a saving in the size of the prime mover at the expense of the region around the upper right hand corner of the rectangle.

Due to the limitation of power the control arrangement must now avoid crossing the power limiting line towards the upper lefthand corner of the graph, to avoid overload or stalling the prime mover.

With power limitation the maximum output torque is now developed at an output speed well below its maximum. Thus there is torque multiplication, as defined in section 2.2 with the torque multiplication factor equal to the apparent power divided by the power of the prime mover. The introduction of power limitation means a higher performance transmission, but economizes on the prime mover. In fig. 3.2–1 the torque multiplication is equal to 3, meaning that the power of the prime mover is only $\frac{1}{3}$ of the apparent power, which represents an important saving in weight and cost. As seen from the graph, only a small part of the rectangle cannot be realized as driving state because it is beyond the power limitation line. The selection of a hydrostatic transmission is thus mainly governed by the torque/speed graph (fig. 3.2–1) of the output shaft and this selection can be summarized by one parameter, the apparent power. In this sense the cost, size and energy loss in the transmission is mainly governed by the apparent power it has to be able to handle. The determination of the real power limit or limit or input power is then a matter of judgment, balancing the sacrifice in performance by the power limitation line, against the saving in size and cost of the prime mover.

The torque and speed limit of the load will not normally coincide with the torque and speedlimit of a suitable hydrostatic secondary unit. Therefore reduction gearing will be required. Since gearing leaves the product of torque and speed unchanged, except for its efficiency loss, both real and apparent power are unaffected by the introduction of reduction gearing.

The matching of a given load to a selected transmission unit through reduction gearing can be further explained by reference to fig. 3.2–2. It is best to proceed from the apparent power of the driven machine and select a hydrostatic transmission that can give the same apparent power, but generally having different torque/speed limits. As an example, such limits are entered in fig. 3.2–2 for the same apparent power. A power limitation line corresponding to a torque multiplication of three is also shown. The required reduction ratio is then simply determined as the ratio of the maximum speed of the secondary unit and of the load.

Naturally the introduction of reduction gearing imposes a penalty in cost and weight on the whole hydrostatic drive. Therefore it is sometimes practical not to use a hydrostatic unit to its full limit in order to be able to have direct coupling between secondary and load. Since in many cases the required rotative speed of the load is much lower than the shaft speed of hydrostatic units, special low speed designs have been developed for hydrostatic units. Nevertheless, the problem of matching the load speed remains even with a slow speed hydrostatic unit, and sometimes some misfit is tolerated in order to avoid reduction gearing.

Summarizing the operation of the transmission with variable

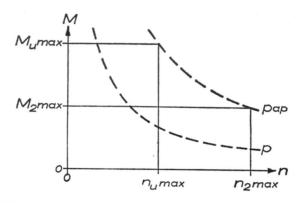

3.2–2 Torque-speed graph for selection of reduction gearing

primary and constant secondary, the increase of torque at low speed is produced by a higher pressure than that needed to produce the highest attainable torque at full output speed. Consequently with high torque multiplication γ within the transmission, the pressure at full output speed and torque becomes rather low, since the highest admissible pressure is limited by the transmission. The disadvantage of the low pressure at high output speed is the greater relative importance of the flow and hydrodynamic losses.

It may appear often advantageous to combine the secondary unit with a suitable reduction gear in one casing, where the hydraulic fluid can also be used to lubricate the gears. A versatile design for such a combined drive box would have some gears easily exchangable in order to give variety of maximum output speeds by fitting gears with a different ratio.

b) *Adaption of variable secondaries*

Hydrostatic transmissions employing variable primaries and variable secondaries are sometimes used, despite mechanical complications and the advantages of this system together with the special problems of adaption to given drive requirements will now be discussed. The principal type is where both the displacement of the primary and of the secondary are varied by the transmission control. The alternative circuit, employing a constant pressure source, consisting of a primary with automatic pressure operated displacement control displacement, and of one or more variable displacement secondaries as shown in fig. 3.1–8 is extremely simple to adapt. Its maximum output torque is given by the system pressure and the maximum displacement of the secondary, and its maximum speed by the speed limit of the same.

Hydrostatic transmissions employing variable primaries and variable secondaries have the following advantages:

1) For some designs of hydrostatic units including axial piston pumps, the limit on shaft speed is higher for a small displacement setting than for full displacement. This increases the apparent power as defined by equation 2.2–2 of the givenunit and makes it more versatile.

2) At very high shaft speeds, with reduced displacement, the flow is not too large and therefore hydrodynamic or flow losses remain within acceptable limits.

3) In a simple transmission a slightly reduced secondary displacement gives a secondary speed higher than the input speed. This may be useful in some drives and may eliminate gears.

4) Since a part of the speed range is covered by varying the secondary, the range of primary variation can be made smaller. This means that the maximum flow in the transmission may be smaller for a given input speed resulting in a smaller and cheaper primary.

Sometimes it is stated that a variable secondary displacement increases the speed range of the hydrostatic transmission. This is only true as long as the speed limit of the secondary increases with reduced displacement, and has to be verified in every instance.

The introduction of variable secondaries does not change the practical method of adaption of hydrostatic transmission to a drive requirement very much. The best way is to determine the apparent power of the driven machine and then select a transmission with at least the same apparent power capability, Then the torque multiplication should be selected, as described in the first part of this section.

The next question, which applies particularly to a hydrostatic transmission with a variable secondary, is how to divide the speed range between primary and secondary control.This is best explained by consideration of the relationship between flow, pressure and the other operating variables shown in fig. 3.2–3.

The upper part of fig. 3.2–3 shows the highest output torque in full line and the highest pressure in dotted line, both as a function of output speed n_2. This is done for two possible divisions, denoted by (a) and (b), of the entire speed range between primary and secondary control. On the lower part of the figures are shown the corresponding flow rates, again as a function of the output speed.

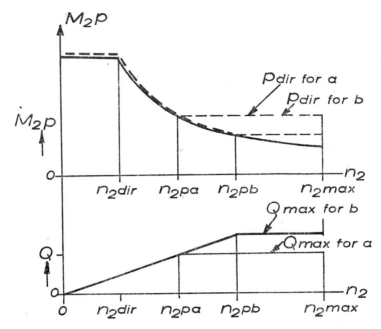

3.2-3 Graph of flow, pressure and output torque against speed with both variable primary and secondary

In the speed range between zero and n_{2dir}, pressure and output torque is limited by the admissible system pressure. In the speed range between n_{2dir} and n_{2pa} or n_{2dir} and n_{2pb} the highest pressure and output torque decreases due to the input power limitation, until at upper end the primary is at almost full displacement. Up to this speed, that is in the range from zero to n_{2pa} or n_{2pb}, output speed is set by primary variation and the flow in the transmission is proportional to output speeds.

In order to obtain higher output speed, the displacement of the secondary is reduced until the speed limit of the secondary is reached. In this range the highest pressure and the flow remains constant, but the highest output torque continues to decrease with the decreasing secondary displacement. Again, the transmission control must not select too small a secondary displacement as this would cause the secondary shaft speed limit to be exceeded with consequent damage.

If the secondary controlled speed range is made large, corresponding to the division "a" of the speed range as in fig. 3.2–3 the pressure during this part of the speed range is higher, and the flow rate is lower.

This means that a smaller primary can be used to produce maximum required flow with a given primary speed. On the other hand, the system will now be subjected to a higher pressure at the upper part of the speed range. From an efficiency point of view a large secondary speed range, case "a", reduces hydrodynamic losses, but increases leakage losses, but increases leakage losses in that range. It should be mentioned, that the maximum displacement of the secondary depends only on the apparent power of the load.

It may be appropriate to mention again, that the highest values of pressure and torque in fig. 3.2–3 are only the maximum admissible values, which must not be exceeded either by incorrect transmission control or overloading. Naturally, the permissible average pressure and therefore the secondary control range depends also on the required duty cycle and life of the installation.

Dry friction losses make it inadvisable in practice to make too small a secondary displacement and the primary speed range should be somewhat larger than the secondary speed range. With both displacements variable, a practical speed range at constant power seems to be 1 to 3 with primary control and 1 to 2 with secondary control, giving a total torque multiplication of 1 to 6. Only in special cases can those figures be exceeded economically.

Summarizing in a hydrostatic transmission with variable second aries, since a part of the torque multiplication is due to variation of the secondary the amount of torque multiplication in the primary can be made smaller.

A smaller primary is therefore required and this makes its adaption to the prime mover easier.

3.3 *Mathematical treatment of hydrostatic transmission*

In this section the behaviour and characteristics of hydrostatic transmission will be treated a little more rigorously by mathematical methods. Instead of complicated algebra, functional diagrams will be used as far as possible, corresponding to the block schemes of control engineering to show the quantitative interrelationships of the operating variables of hydrostatic transmissions. The properties of functional and structural diagrams are treated in more detail in Appendix 2.

Positive torques and speeds will only be considered with the transmission driving the output shaft in one sense of rotation against an opposing torque provided by the load. There is nothing to prevent either speed or torque becoming negative, corresponding to reversing and braking the output shaft as treated in section 2.6. In this case other operating variables such as displacement, pressure or flow may become negative, but the functional diagrams in fig. 3.3–1 to 3.3–8 remain valid. The only point to observe is that the various torque losses are always opposed to the sense of rotation of the corresponding hydrostatic units.

a) *Functional diagrams for variable primary transmissions*

This part is concerned with the variable primary hydrostatic transmission, with hydraulic circuits figs. 3.1–3 and 3.1–4. A simple functional diagram of this transmission appears in fig. 3.3–1, which is similar to fig. 2.1–2. The control signal is the primary displacement setting a, which enters the first block on the left. Its output is the

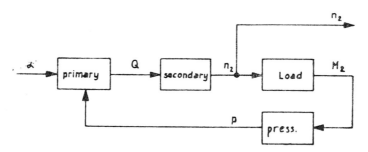

3.3–1 Fundamental functional diagram of variable primary transmission

flow Q, which enters the block representing the secondary. The output of this block is the shaft speed n_2, which is the useful output variable and which also enters the block representing the load. The output or reaction of the load is the opposing torque M_2, which produces, through the block in the lower line, the system pressure p. The pressure influences slightly the flow produced by the primary with a given displacement setting a because of leakage. This influence is represented by the feedback connection entering the block representing the pumping function of the primary. In this functional diagram the shaft speed is taken as the transmission effect, and the feedback of the load torque as the disturbing influence.

In order to obtain a more complete functional diagram, the mathematical relationships between the different operating variables are inserted in the different blocks. These relationships are given by the fundamental equations (1.1–2), (1.1–3) and (1.2–8) and the resulting

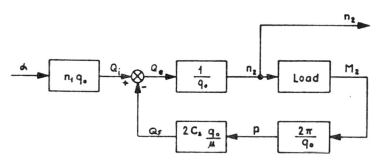

3.3-2 Mathematical functional diagram of variable primary transmission

functional diagram in fig. 3.3-2. Naturally, the relationship between secondary shaft speed and torque depends on the load and cannot be specified from the transmission properties alone. However, for a certain load it will always be possible to find a functional quantitative relationship between speed and torque, which may perhaps include terms proportional to the change of shaft speed or acceleration due to inertia effects on the load. The influence of the system pressure on the flow in fig. 3.3-2 is now represented by the slip flow Q_{ie}, which must be deducted from the ideal flow to obtain the effective flow giving the shaft speed. Since there will be leakage both in the primary and the secondary, a factor 2 appears in the relationship between pressure and slip flow, in the left lower block.

The functional diagram fig. 3.3-2 gives the secondary shaft speed as a function of the primary displacement setting, but ignores the primary shaft speed and torque. Although the limits on both these variables and on the other variables such as system pressure and secondary speed are not included in this figure, it should be mentioned that the transmission control must ensure that none of the operating variables can exceed their safe or economical limits.

On the alternative functional diagram (fig. 3.3-3) both primary speed and torque are included. This is done by the pressure connection entering the lower right hand block which represents the relationship between system pressure and primary torque. The torque enters the block representing the prime mover, which produces the primary speed. Since variations of this speed are a disturbing influence on the flow with a given displacement setting, there is a cross connection to the upper left hand block representing the flow. Furthermore there is a cross connection showing the influence of primary displacement setting on the relation between system pressure and primary torque.

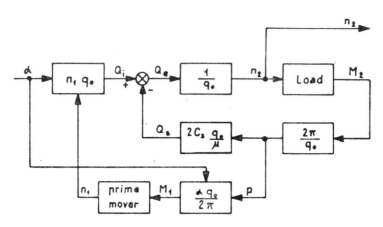

3.3-3 Functional diagram of variable primary transmission including variation of input speed

With two cross connections the functional diagram fig. 3.3–3 is no longer linear, because two of the blocks represent a multiplication of the operating variables. This follows the fundamental equations of hydrostatic units, which state that flow is the product of shaft speed and displacement setting and torque the product of pressure and displacement setting. Both blocks which have non linearity refer to the functioning of the primary. This functional diagram is useful in investigating the influence of a variable primary speed for the relationship between displacement setting α and the secondary speed. Such variations may occur because of the torque speed characteristics of an electric induction motor, or from imperfect governing of a diesel engine. The primary torque must not exceed a certain value to avoid stalling of the prime mover. Normally either the characteristics or the governing of the prime mover maintains the primary speed within acceptable limits.

In most cases fig. 3.3–2 is an adequate mathematical representation of hydrostatic transmission with variable primary and fixed secondary. It should be noted that q_o in the first upper block of this figure refers to the primary, while the same letter in the second upper block refers to the maximum displacement of the secondary. If one uses a secondary of different maximum displacement a different notation must be employed. For a practical design, one determines the secondary displacement from the maximum output torque and highest allowable pressure, and then the maximum flow rates from the output speed. Next the input speed is chosen to provide sufficient flow including slip flow. If the calculated input speed is

not practicable one can alter maximum displacement of the primary
as described in section 3.2 on reduction gearing.

The effect of the various torque losses both in primary and secondary are included in the functional diagram fig. 3.3–4. In particular,
the secondary lorque losses are added to the torque of the load to

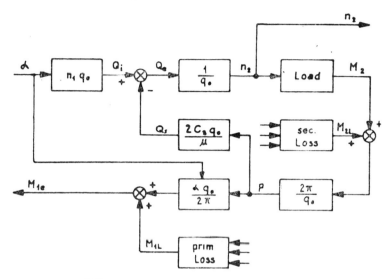

3.3–4 Functional diagram of variable primary transmission including primary
and secondary torque losses

give the torque determining the pressure. The torque loss in the
primary is added to that required to produce pressure to give the
effective torque required from the prime mover. The arrows show
that the torque losses depend on the different operating variables, as
given by equations 1.2–1—1.2–5. It is possible to represent the
torque losses as dry and viscous friction and hydrodynamical loss,
and make connections and include blocks for the appropriate variables such as flow, speed pressure etc., but this is unnecessary for
our purpose.

The question whether it is possible to neglect the torque loss
depends on the operating variables, but it is often possible to do so
at full power. On the other hand, with a free output shaft, all the
pressure, necessarily small, comes from the secondary torque plus
part of the pressure loss in the main circuit.

The secondary speed as function of the load torque can be read from the functional diagram fig. 3.3–2, neglecting both primary and secondary torque losses.

$$n_2 = an_1 - \frac{4\pi i^2_3 C_s}{q_0\,\mu} M_1 \qquad\qquad .. \qquad (3.3\text{--}1)$$

This allows the slip coefficient C_s to be determined from the torque speed curves of the transmission.

All the functional diagrams so far in this section have shown the flow and secondary speed as an effect of the transmission control. The effect of the load torque and pressure is a disturbing influence which must be fed back to the appropriate block. This is preferable because during normal operation the influence of the output torque on flow rate and speed is small. However, for the exceptional case of blocked or stalled output shaft, the effective flow is zero and for a given transmission control setting the output torque is determined by the leakage as long as the displacement setting is quite small. With any substantial displacement, the pressure rises high enough as to open the relief valve or to damage some part of the transmission.

b) *Functional diagrams with reference values*

For the practical determination of the operating variables it is useful to employ the reference values of speed, pressure, flow, etc. as introduced in section 1.2. This means that instead of the equation (3.3–1) the actual values of the variables are expressed as multiples

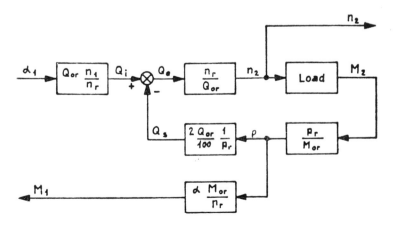

3.3–5 Functional diagram of variable primary transmission using reference values of operating variables

of the corresponding reference values. As mentioned before the reference values are those obtained at a basic values of speed, pressure, etc., e.g. 1 500 rpm. 100 kgf/cm² (1 420 psi) and full displacement give the reference flow and lossfree torque.

A functional diagram using reference values for the operating variables of a hydrostatic transmission with variable primary and fixed secondary is shown in fig. 3.3–5. It may be worthwhile to explain this functional diagram in greater detail.

The first block in the upper line of fig. 3.3–5 is the ideal flow of the primary.

$$Q_i = a_1 \, n_1 \, q_0 = a_1 \frac{n_1}{n_r} Q_{or} \qquad .. \quad (3.3\text{--}2)$$

The effective flow is obtained by deduction of the slip flow and the secondary speed is determined from the following equation, represented by the second block in the upper line of the figure.

$$n_2 = \frac{Q_e}{q_0} = n_r \frac{Q_e}{Q_{or}} \qquad .. \quad (3.3\text{--}3)$$

This equation gives the relationship of speed and flow if, for example, the flow 60% of the reference flow Q_{or}, the output speed n_2 is also 60% of the reference speed n_r.

The next block gives the torque opposing the secondary shaft speed as a function of the load. The last block in the second line gives the system pressure.

$$p = \frac{2\pi M_2}{q_0} = p_r \frac{M_2}{M_{or}} \qquad .. \quad (3.3\text{--}4)$$

Finally the slip flow Q_s is determined by the first block in the second line from

$$Q_s = 2C_s \frac{p}{\mu} \, q_0 = 2 \, Q_{sr} \frac{p}{p_r} = Q_{or} \frac{1}{100} \frac{p}{p_r} \qquad .. \quad (3.3\text{--}5)$$

The last form of this equation has also been included in the first block of the second line of fig. 3.3–5.

For the relationship between secondary speed and torque one obtains by combination of the equations (3.3–2)—(3.3–5)

$$n_2 = an_1 - 2 \frac{Q_{sr}}{Q_{or}} \frac{M_2}{M_{or}} n_r \qquad .. \quad (3.3\text{--}6)$$

7

In the last form of equation (3.3–5) above, the supposition is made, as in equation 1.2–2, that the reference slip flow is 1% of the reference flow at the reference pressure, which is typical for axial piston hydrostatic units. The total slip flow, which is 2% of reference flow at reference pressure because of leakage in both primary and secondary, is deducted from the ideal flow to obtain the effective flow for the secondary speed. Thus the leakage is a small percentage of the reference flow, but it becomes much more important when the primary displacement is reduced.

As an example, in a hydrostatic transmission working with a torque multiplication of three, with the above leakage, one has

$$a = \frac{1}{3} \qquad p = 3\,p_r$$

$$Q_i = \frac{1}{3}Q_{or} \; ; \quad Q_s = 3\,Q_{or}\,\frac{2}{100}$$

which gives

$$\frac{Q_s}{Q_i} = \frac{18}{100} \qquad \qquad \text{.. \quad (3.3–7)}$$

Equation (3.3–7) implies a slip of 18% for a transmission working at full power at a torque multiplication of 3. This is because, with high pressure and low flow the relative importance of the slip flow is increased. Therefore in a hydrostatic transmission with only primary control, a torque multiplication of about 3 is the highest practicable, unless hydrostatic units with smaller leakages or slip flows are used.

Naturally it would have been possible to include in fig. 3.3–5 the block representing the torque losses in primary and secondary analogous to fig. 3.3–4 using reference values. This is useful when discussing the torque losses and presents no difficulty, but it is not needed for the purpose of this book. Summarizing the functional diagrams of fig. 3.3–6, they are strictly equivalent to the equations 3.3–2—3.3–6, but give a simpler and clearer representation of the quantitative situation. They are thus a striking example of the advantages of functional diagrams over mathematical equations.

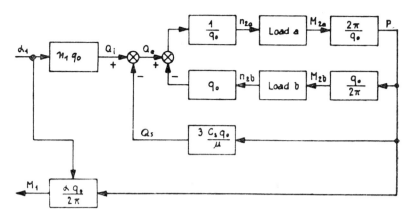

3.3-6 Functional diagram of transmission with two secondaries in parallel

c) *Transmission with variable primaries and two secondaries in parallel*

The functional diagram of a hydrostatic transmission with one variable primary and two constant secondaries all of the same maximum displacement, is represented on fig. 3.3-6. Here the effective flow splits into two parts, corresponding to the two secondaries in parallel. Then in each branch we have the usual chain between flow, secondary speed, secondary torque and pressure. The pressure is fed backwards through the branch (b) of the functional diagram, so giving torque, speed and the flow Q_b, which is deducted from the effective flow to give the flow entering branch (a). Naturally both branches are equal and this form is needed to represent the division of flow between both secondaries in the functional diagram.

From the pressure one determines the slip flow, here increased because there are now three hydrostatic units in parallel. This slip flow is deducted as before from the ideal flow of the primary to obtain the effective flow giving the speed of the secondary.

d) *Variable secondary with constant primary*

It is also possible to draw a functional diagram for the hydrostatic transmission using a variable secondary with a constant primary. This includes the upper speed range with secondary control of a transmission where both primary and secondary are variable. The functional diagram is shown in fig. 3.3-7 where the ideal flow is

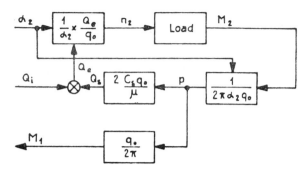

3.3–7 Functional diagram of transmission with constant primary and variable secondary

now fixed by the primary speed and displacement. The secondary speed is given from the effective flow by the following form of the fundamental equation

$$n_2 = \frac{Q_e}{q_0} \times \frac{1}{a_2} \qquad\qquad .. \quad (3.3\text{–}8)$$

The pressure depends on the load torque, and the reciprocal of the secondary displacement as shown in the right hand block in the second line of fig. 3.3–7. As before the pressure determines the slip flow and the primary torque.

It should be noted that this system is not linear, because of the reciprocal relationship between flow and shaft speed and between load torque and pressure. This is not a practical disadvantage, but it makes calculation by traditional methods more difficult.

e) *Variable secondary with constant pressure*

A hydrostatic transmission incorporating a source of constant hydraulic pressure and a secondary with controlled displacement has many attractive features, as mentioned in section 3.1–3. Its functional diagram is shown in fig. 3.3–8.

In fig. 3.3–8 the secondary displacement produces a torque in accordance with the fundamental equation (1.2–8). This torque, after deduction of the torques losses enters the block representing the load, to produce the secondary speed. The dry friction loss with constant pressure makes the torque loss constant independent of displacement setting and speed. On the other hand, both viscous and hydrodynamic torque losses depend on the operating variables, and

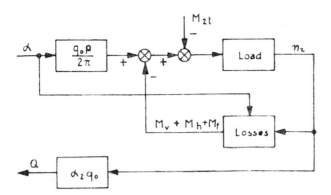

3.3–8 Functional diagram of transmission with constant pressure and variable secondary

are deducted from the ideal torque to give the torque available on the load. As the torque losses are small compared to the ideal torque, the torque available at the load is almost independent of secondary speed, and proportional to secondary displacement, as long as the pressure remains constant. The flow required is obtained from the secondary speed as shown in the lowest block.

It should be noted that this hydrostatic transmission gives a torque which is proportional to the secondary displacement setting and is nearly independent of shaft speed, except for the effect of torque losses. Where the load torque is independent of speed the displacement setting controls the acceleration of the output shaft and the secondary displacement setting must be controlled carefully to avoid excessive speed. There are many types of load where the torque is very nearly independent of speed, e.g. vehicles running slowly on smooth surfaces, winches and cutting tools. This problem of acceleration control and possible instability is wellknown in control engineering as are the methods of dealing with it. Since the system is linear, calculation by the usual mathematical methods of control engineering is possible.

3.4 *Experiments with hydrostatic transmission*

Because of the great versatility of hydrostatic transmission many interesting experiments are possible with quite simple installations. There are two purposes for experimenting with hydrostatic transmission, either as a functional test, or to determine efficiency in a particular set of circumstances and operating variables. The normal users acceptance test is an example of a functional test.

a) *Direct transmission test*

A proposed arrangement for a direct transmission test is shown in fig. 3.4–1. The test stand consists of constant speed prime mover, in industrial practice normally AC induction motor, which drives the primary directly. The fixed displacement secondary drives a combined continuously rated dynamometer brake such as is available commercially. Both primary and secondary shaft speeds are measured by suitable speedometers, and a pressure gauge is fitted to the delivery line. The secondary torque is measured by the dynamometer and its value for a given speed can be manually adjusted on the dynamometer. The auxiliary valves described in section 3.1 are omitted to simplify the figure.

For efficiency determination it is also necessary to measure the torque on the primary. This can be done either by determination of the torque reaction of a pivot suspended electric motor, preferably in special antifriction bearings, or more simply, in industry, by a three-phase kilowatt meter (fig. 3.4–1). In order to calibrate the kilowatt meter in effective torque, the electric motor can be connected directly to the dynamometer and the latter can be used for calibration. For consistent results with factory mains it is necessary to use a kilowattmeter measuring the power in all three phases. Only such an instrument, which is commercially available, will give a correct indication as the loads in the phases are usually appreciably out of balance. It is also desirable to record the primary displacement

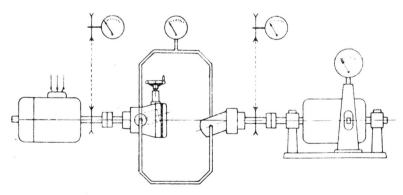

3.4–1 Transmission test with commercial dynamometer with electric motor as prime mover

a_1. One interesting test is to vary the secondary torque on the dynamometer whilst maintaining the secondary speed constant. This is done by increasing the primary displacement by the amount needed to make up the leakage due to the slip displacement. This can be expressed by the equation

$$n_2 = n_1(a_1 - a_s) ; \qquad a_s = 2C_s \frac{p}{n_1 \mu} \qquad \qquad .. \quad (3.4\text{--}1)$$

which is obtained by using the definition (1.2–2) for the slip displacement. If the secondary torque cannot be measured for any reason the pressure as shown by the pressure gauge will give an estimation of this torque sufficient for the determination of the slip displacement from this equation.

In normal operation the efficiency is obtained as the quotient of output and input power, which are both proportional to the product of speed and torque. As explained in section 1.4 with hydrostatic units, it is very difficult to obtain the efficiency with acceptable accuracy hydrostatic transmissions of the usual high efficiency. If a commercial dynamometer which is an expensive piece of equipment, should not be available, it is possible to use an ajustable displacement hydrostatic pumping unit instead

The dynamometer unit is preferably mounted in the tank and the delivery passed through an adjustable relief valve returned to the tank. The equivalent of the power loss appears as heat in the oil and

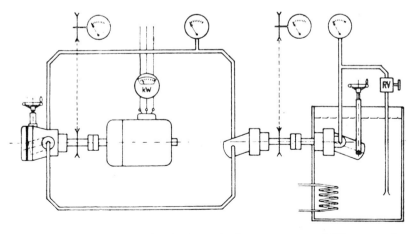

3.4–2 Transmission test with hydrostatic dynamometer, and Wattmeter in electric mains for approximative primary torque indication

it is necessary to install a cooler as shown. An actual installation of
this type is shown in fig. 3.4–3, with the electric motor in the centre,
the primary on the right, and to the left, first the secondary and then
the hydrostatic dynamometer unit. It is used to test the dynamometer unit at various speeds and also the hydrostatic transmission.
It can be easily converted to regenerative testing by turning the
secondary round.

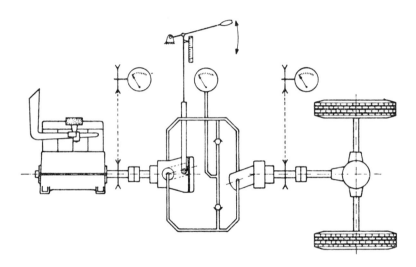

3.4–3 Actual test installation with hydrostatic unit as dynamometer on
the left

This is a very versatile dynamometer and a suitable one for continuous service, because both the displacement and the pressure can
be adjusted, the latter by manipulating the relief valve. It is possible
to eliminate the errors due to the various torque losses in the dynamometer unit by making preliminary calibration runs, at different
values of displacement and pressure for each torque to be measured.

At the same time the performance and efficiency of the dynamometer unit can be tested at various shaft speeds as produced by
the hydrostatic transmission. This is preferable to and less costly
than a Ward Leonard electric variable speed drive. Unfortunately
the accuracy of this hydrostatic dynamometer tends to be limited
by the low accuracy of normally available pressure gauges, but if a
precision free piston pressure gauge, having a weight loaded rotating
piston is used, very high accuracy can be obtained. Naturally it will

be necessary to provide an accurate scale indicating the displacement of the hydrostatic dynamometer unit.

Alternatively, it would also be possible to mount the entire hydrostatic dynamometer, consisting of hydrostatic unit, pressure gauge, relief valve and displacement setting mechanism on a pivoting bearing as is usual with dynamometers, and to measure reaction torque by a suitable reaction arm. This would completely eliminate any errors due to torque losses or gauge inaccuracies, and the errors resulting from the oil entering and leaving through an open jet could be kept very small, but the author has not yet seen such a pivoted hydrostatic dynamometer.

Some times it is preferable to use an internal combustion engine instead of an electric motor as a prime mover, especially for higher powers and when the noise is not objectionable. The engine must necessarily be speed governed in order to prevent overspeeding under no-load conditions. With diesel engines, the position of the injection rack may be used as an approximate indication of the torque developed by the engine.

If the performance of an engine-driven hydrostatic transmission is disappointing, it would be advisable to recheck the torque actually supplied by the engine. Many engines do not reach the specified torque until after prolonged running, and it may quickly deteriorate after maintenance. Therefore if the continuous torque measuring

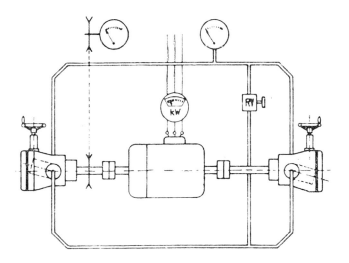

3.4–4 Transmission installed in motor car as rolling test rig

equipment is not available, it would be worthwhile to recalibrate the engine after a test run, by coupling it directly to the dynamometer. At this point it should be mentioned that it is possible to obtain commercially, torque meters incorporating strain gauges and electronic indication; the comparative modest outlay for such equipment will be well worth while if the test stand is in frequent use.

An interesting variant is to install the hydrostatic transmission in a motor car, (fig. 3.4–4). Here the minimum instrumentation is a pressure gauge, speedometers for primary and secondary speed and an accurate scale for the variable displacement setting. This is a very versatile rolling test rig, where a variety of load conditions can be demonstrated to prospective customers. Again the actual torque of the engine has to be evaluated since it will depend, in addition to the maintenance status, on such variables as barometric pressure and humidity.

A second variant of the direct transmission test is to load the secondary shaft with a flywheel instead of a dynamometer. With constant secondary speed the torque is then quite low, and substantial torques are produced by changing the secondary speed through the transmission control lever. The advantage of this test is that the power consumption is low, since the transmission returns power from the flywheel through the electric induction motor to the power mains when braking.

A transmission loaded with a flywheel for testing purposes was shown on fig. I–4. With the dimensions shown the torque required to maintain constant secondary speed is very low, corresponding to less than 10 kgf/cm^2 (140 psi) pressure at full speed (1 500 rpm), but the rated torque of the transmission can be produced with quite low rate of change of secondary speed.

This variable speed drive loaded with only a flywheel is also an interesting demonstration of the fact that the torque is, momentarily, independent of speed. Indeed with any given speed, torque of any magnitude and direction can be produced by suitable changing of the transmission control lever. With the large flywheel shown on fig. I–4, torque produced in this way changes the secondary speed only slowly and rapid manipulation of the transmission control lever results in overpressure and the relief valve blowing.

b) *Regenerative test*

In order to avoid the waste of power due to braking the output shaft of the transmission under test, one may be tempted to couple the secondary to the prime mover in so that the torque produced by

the secondary is returned to the prime mover. This is not only possible but actually very simple, because in the arrangement in fig.
3.4–2, one only has to disconnect secondary from the dynamometer,
turn it around and couple it to the other end of the electric motor
shaft. The only difficulty is with the slip flow or leakage because, as
they are both coupled to the motor shaft, primary and secondary
always run at the same speed and it will usually be necessary to use a
variable displacement secondary unit as in fig. 3.4–5.

The analysis of the operation of the regenerative rig in fig. 3.4–5
depends on the fact that the sum of the flows of the primary and
secondary and of the slip flow must be zero, or in other words the
primary flow must be equal to the sum of the secondary flow and the
slip flow. In consequence, the secondary displacement must always
be somewhat smaller than the primary displacement, making it
necessary to use a secondary of variable displacement, but the primary can be of fixed displacement. Using equation 1.2–1 with primary
displacement equal to 1, one obtains, letting $a_1 = 1$

$$n_1 q_0 = n_1 a_2 q_0 + 2 C_s \frac{p}{\mu} q_0 \qquad .. \qquad (3.4\text{–}2)$$

From this one obtains the pressure by simple manipulation

$$p = \frac{\mu}{2C_s} n_1 (1 - a_2) \qquad .. \qquad (3.4\text{–}3)$$

Equation (3.4–3) can be used to measure the slip coefficient C_s
from the secondary displacement a_2. No pressure is developed with
full secondary displacement.

Alternatively, in practice is often more convenient to express the
preceding equation using the reference values of pump flow and slip
flow, as defined by the equations (1.2–11) and (1.2–12). Here, preferably, the shaft speed is taken as the reference speed n_r so that one
obtains

$$Q_{or} = a_2 Q_{or} + \frac{2p}{p_r} Q_{sr}$$

It should be mentioned again that Q_{sr} is the slip flow of one unit at
the reference pressure (normally taken as 100 kgf/cm² (1 420 psi).

From this we obtain by simple manipulation

$$p = \frac{p_r}{2} \frac{Q_{or}}{Q_{sr}} (1 - a_2) \qquad .. \qquad (3.4\text{–}4)$$

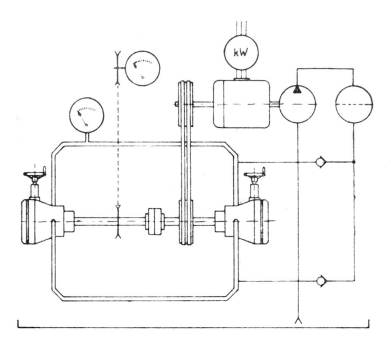

3.4–5 Regenerative test with both hydrostatic units coupled to prime mover

Both preceding equations show how carefully one has to manipulate the secondary displacement a_2 in order to select the system pressure for the regenerative test. If, as mentioned previously, the reference slip flow is 1% of the reference flow of the unit ($Q_{sr}/Q_{or} =$ 1/100) a reduction of the secondary displacement from its full value by only 2% is necessary in order to produce reference pressure in the system. Further reduction of secondary displacement increases the system pressure proportionally with consequent danger of damage from pressure surges.

In order to consider the torques of the regenerative test, one uses the loss moment as defined by equation 1.2–7. This loss moment is additive to the primary torque and deductive from the secondary torque. Denoting the torque supplied by the prime mover by M_{pm} one obtains the following equation, showing that the driving torque must be equal to the braking torque

$$M_{pm} + \frac{a_2 p q_o}{2\pi} - M_1 = \frac{p q_o}{2\pi} + M_1 \qquad \text{..} \qquad (3.4\text{--}5)$$

Alternative form of fixed output shaft test with tied vehicle and pull measurement

If one assumes that the torque loss is equal for primary and secondary, which is certainly justified because their difference in displacement is very small, one obtains for the required torque of the prime mover by manipulation of the previous equation:—

$$M_{pm} = \frac{pq_o}{2\pi}(1-a_2)+2M_1 \qquad .. \qquad (3.4\text{--}6)$$

The torque of the prime mover is thus equal to the torque required to make up for the leakage and to the torque loss for both hydrostatic units. Using again the reference values defined in section 1.2–2, one obtains from the previous equation

$$M_{pm} = M_{or}\frac{p}{p_r}(1-a_2)+2M_1 \qquad .. \qquad (3.4\text{--}7)$$

Since secondary displacement is very nearly equal to unity the torque of the prime mover is very small compared to reference torque, or to the torque of the unit in normal operation. Measuring the prime mover torque M_{pm}, the torque losses can be determined with sufficient accuracy by equation (3.4–7) if it is possible to read the secondary displacement precisely. This should not be too difficult and any provisional scale for the secondary displacement setting can be calibrated by using a flow meter at low pressure. In any case the required torque from the prime mover in the regenerative test is only a small fraction of the torque required in the direct test, resulting in a substantial economy in the size of the prime mover, in addition to the inherently higher accuracy of the measurements, as mentioned.

The torque actually taken by a hydrostatic unit in the regenerative test is the reference torque at reference pressure, and proportionally more at higher system pressures. This applies a greater torque to the motor shaft than does the power produced by the motor. Fortunately this usually causes no trouble. An i.c. engine crankshaft on the other hand might fail under this treatment.

It is sometimes preferable to couple two units directly through one shaft, and to feed in from the prime mover the torque required to make up for losses, as shown in fig. 3.4–6. This is a very instructive example of a regenerative test, with the loss made up mechanically. It should be noted that the chain drive has only to be able to carry the torque of the prime mover. The other shaft and of the electric motor can be used to drive a priming pump as shown. The necessary auxiliary valves are not shown in the figure.

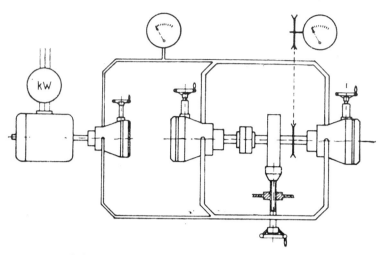

3.4–6 Regenerative test with mechanical make-up

As an alternative arrangement of a regenerative test, it is possible to make up for the losses hydraulically, as shown in fig. 3.4–7. Here both main hydrostatic units are coupled together, and a third electrically driven hydrostatic pump is provided which is put hydraulically in parallel to the main units. Since it is used only to make up for losses it can be relatively small. In order to produce pressure in this circuit it is necessary to provide a mechanical brake on the shaft between both main hydrostatic units. Then the speed of the main units adjusts itself until the difference of flow of both main units (because of different displacement settings) is equal to the make-up flow minus the leakages. Thus, if both main units are set to nearly equal displacement overspeeding may occur. The system pressure can be derived from the fact that the torque due to the system pressure and the difference of displacement between the main units is equal to the torque produced by the brake plus the torque losses in both main units.

In practice great care has to be exercised in operating a regenerative test with hydraulic make-up in order to avoid overspeeds and over pressures. For starting it is best to set the primary displacement to zero and the secondary displacement to maximum and to release the brake. On starting the make-up pump, the transmission will revolve slowly. As the primary displacement is increased, the transmission will begin to pick up speed, and pressure will develop corresponding to the torque losses. When the desired transmission speed is reached, pressure can further be increased by applying the brake. If

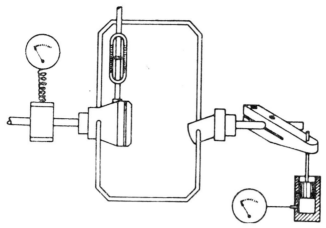

3.4–7 Regenerative test with hydraulic make-up and mechanical brake

the displacements of both main units are made nearly equal the system pressure even with the brake off will increase indefinitely and the transmission may become selflocking. During the experiment the transmission leakage is given by the make-up flow, less the flow as determined by the transmission speed and the difference in displacements. The torque loss can be determined from the torque defined by the system pressure, the maximum displacement of both units and the difference of the displacement settings, and then deducting any torque applied by the brake. Generally this test is a little less suitable for precise determination of efficiency and torque losses, but it is sometimes used as a functional test because of the simplicity of the mechanical installation needed to produce a high torque.

It would also be easily possible to provide a mathematical theory for the regenerative test with hydraulic make-up, similar to the theories presented above for mechanical make-up but this will not be needed for the purpose of this book.

c) *Free and fixed output shaft test*

A further test on hydrostatic transmission with free and fixed output shaft is analogous to the open and blocked port test on hydrostatic units described in section 1.4 c. It consists in measuring the primary torque firstly, with open freely revolving secondary shaft as function of the primary displacement, and in secondly with a clamped secondary shaft noting also the primary displacement required to produce the pressure and secondary torque.

3.4–8 Scheme of test with fixed output shaft

There are two variants, depending on the installation available, which can be considerably simpler than that needed for the full test previously described. A suitable test arrangement is shown in fig. 3.4–8. The primary has a displacement scale, pressure gauge and primary torque meter. The secondary shaft revolves freely during the first part of the test and is clamped during the second part. It is desirable to have a device to measure secondary torque with fixed shaft. This can take the form shown with a beam loading a hydraulic piston in a cylinder with a pressure gauge.

Instead of the cylinder for secondary torque measurement, it would be possible to use weights suspended on the beam, and generally there is no limit to the amount of ingenuity that can be used to improvise a torque measuring device on the stationary output shaft. In the case of a vehicle it can be attached to a fixed point by a cable with a pull measuring device as shown in fig. 3.4–8 for a small locomotive. For a winch the attachment of the cable on a fixed point is very simple. Naturally some error is introduced by friction in final reduction gears, but nevertheless an improvised test of this kind gives interesting information. If no secondary torque measuring device can be found, it is necessary to use the indication gained from the main pressure gauge, which neglects dry friction in the secondary.

For the free shaft measurement in a vehicle, the rolling resistance has to be considered, but it should be possible to jack up the locomotive in fig. 3.4–8 to provide free rotation of the wheels or to temporarily disconnect the secondary.

If no primary torque measuring device can be found, it can be approximately determined from the position of the governor or of the injection rack of the engine, or else from a small flowmeter in the fuel pipe measuring the fuel consumption rate of the engine.

The interpretation of the free shaft measurement begins by noting that dry friction and leakage are neglegible because of the low pressure. With diminishing primary displacement the transmission takes only the primary friction torque, whilst with increasing displacement the secondary viscous friction torque and the hydrodynamic torque losses are added.

For quantitative analysis it is expedient to use reference values with the primary speed equal to the reference speed ($n_1 = n_r$) and to suppose that the primary and secondary are identical units having the same leakage and torque loss characteristics. Noting that $n_2 = a_1 n_1$ to a high degree of accuracy with a free shaft:

$$M_{los} = M_{vr}(1+a_1)+2M_{hr}a^3 \qquad .. \qquad (3.4\text{--}8)$$

where M_{los} is the torque loss absorbed by the primary in the open shaft condition. The equation (3.4–8) represents quantitatively the absorption of the viscous friction in the primary with zero displacement setting and the increase due to secondary viscous friction and hydrodynamical losses with increasing displacement. For proper loss separation it is again advisable to use a graphical representation similar to the treatment in section 1.4–c—figs. 1.4–4 and 1.4–5.

In the fixed shaft experiment, hydrodynamic losses and secondary viscous friction disappear, so that the primary torque is expended in leakage losses and dry and viscous friction in the primary. Letting again $n_1 = n_r$ one obtains by inserting the torque loss of equation 1.2–17 and 1.2–18

$$M_{1bs} = 2a_s\frac{p}{p_r}M_{or}+\frac{p}{p_r}M_{fr}+M_{vr} \qquad .. \qquad (3.4\text{--}9)$$

where M_{1bs} is the torque absorbed by the primary in the fixed shaft condition. The factor 2 arises because there is leakage in two hydrostatic units. The value $2a_s$ is read directly on the primary displacement scale. With zero primary displacement, only its viscous friction is absorbed and thus easily measured. With some primary displacement, the first term of equation (3.4–9) can be determined from the observed pressure and displacement, so that by subtraction one obtains the dry friction of the primary. In a sense, as in section 1.4–c the leakage of the transmission is again determined by the slip displacement setting required to produce a certain pressure.

For the relationship between pressure and secondary torque it is

8

to be noted, that with fixed shaft dry friction is the only torque loss in the secondary. Therefore one obtains for the torque in analogy to equation (1.2–21).

$$M_{2bs} = \frac{p}{p_r}M_{or} + \frac{p}{p_r}M_{fr} = \frac{p}{p_r}M_{or}\left(1 + \frac{M_{fr}}{M_{or}}\right) \quad .. \quad (3.4\text{–}10)$$

where M_{2bs} is the measured secondary torque in the blocked shaft condition.

Equation (3.4–10) enables the secondary dry friction to be determined from measurements of the torque and pressure. Although this is not strictly necessary because dry friction can be determined— from equation (3.4–9) it is interesting as a check on the behaviour of dry friction with fixed output shaft.

The preceding relations allow all the loss components to be determined separately by measurement of the primary torque, pressure and displacement setting in the free and fixed shaft condition. If the primary displacement, particularly with fixed shaft, cannot be measured it is necessary to use a different method, as follows:

Replacing α_s by M_s as defined by equation (1.2–18) with $n = n_r$ one obtains

$$M_{1bs} = 2\left(\frac{p}{p_r}\right)^2 \frac{Q_{sr}}{Q_{or}}M_{or} + \frac{p}{p_r}M_{fr} + M_{vr} \quad .. \quad (3.4\text{–}11)$$

which contains the leakage and dry friction of the primary as pressure dependent losses. By measuring the primary torque with fixed secondary shaft as a function of pressure this is determined and leakage and dry friction can be separated by measuring the latter with the aid of equation (3.4–10).

As with the hydrostatic units in section 1.4–c the free shaft experiments give approximately the losses needed to produce output speed, while the fixed shaft experiments give the losses required to produce pressure. Therefore the loss at any secondary speed and pressure is given by the free and fixed shaft losses, deducting the primary viscous friction, as it is included in both experiments.

For a quantitative representation it is preferable to refer to the power losses, which are proportional to the primary torque since the primary speed is constant. Remembering that secondary speed is exactly proportional to primary displacement in the open port experiment, because the pressure is neglegible, the power loss at any secondary speed and pressure can be represented as

$$P_1(n_2, p) = P_{los}(n_2) + P_{1bs}(p) - P_{los}(\alpha_1 = 0) \qquad (3.4\text{–}12)$$

where P_{los} and P_{lbs} are the power losses of the entire transmission in the free and fixed shaft condition. In order to relate this power loss to secondary torque instead of to pressure, the secondary dry friction has to be considered using equation (3.4–10). Since the corresponding power loss is proportional to the product of secondary speed and secondary torque it does not admit of the simple interpretation of equation (3.4–12) but it can be added afterwards as a correction. In engineering approximation the secondary dry friction is often neglected.

The fixed output shaft experiment approximates closely the definition of stalled torque multiplication γ_s in section 2.5. Indeed with primary speed equal to maximum secondary speed, the stalled torque multiplication is equal to the ratio of the secondary torque M_{2bs} to the primary torque M_{1bs} in the fixed output shaft experiment. Since the pressure is determined here from the secondary torque by equation (3.4–10) and the primary torque in terms of pressure by equation (3.1–11), the stalled torque multiplication can be determined directly by algebraic manipulation of both equations. The resulting formula is a little complicated, because equation (3.4–11) is quadratic for pressure and will not be reproduced here. It would give the stalled torque multiplication in terms of the reference torque losses and leakage as a function of secondary torque. Since the primary torque is a quadratic function of pressure and secondary torque, the torque multiplication at stall is smaller for high secondary torques, because of the power consumption due to leakage.

The free and fixed shaft transmission experiments described here are only approximate, because the formula representing the dependence of the various losses on the operating variables are themselves only approximate, as mentioned in section 1.2. Nevertheless they permit interesting experiments on hydrostatic transmissions with a minimum amount of equipment at the factory or even if the transmission has already been supplied to the customer and installed at its destination.

CHAPTER 4

CONTROL OF HYDROSTATIC UNITS AND TRANSMISSION

Section 4.1 *Actuation and Control*

The control of hydrostatic transmission has as part of its purpose, the production of a variable and controlled secondary speed and avoidance of undesirable values of any operating variables, such as excessive pressure, torque or input power. Except for the occasional use of valves in high speed low-power servomechanisms, control of hydrostatic transmissions is effected by changing the displacement of the hydrostatic unit. There are many ways of effecting this displacement setting, but the forces required are substantial and necessitate in many cases servo or power-assisted operation.

The magnitude of the actuating forces depends on the details of the hydrostatic unit valving, that is the admission and release of the fluid at the dead centres of piston travel. The force required to hold the displacement setting of an axial piston unit in any position fluctuates with double the piston frequency. In the absence of friction it is approximately equal to one quarter of the force of one piston multiplied by its stroke and divided by the length of travel of the actuation pivot required for changing the displacement from zero to maximum. It is advisable to make the force output of the actuator at least 50% greater than this to allow for friction etc.

Since the piston forces are proportional to the pressure, actuation forces are also proportional to it.

The simplest control is a handwheel actuator mounted on the spindle, usually with a self locking travelling nut and this is quite satisfactory for a slow change of displacement setting. As shown in fig. 4.1–1 it is necessary to provide a displacement setting indicator which can take the form of a pointer travelling on a scale. In the terminology of modern systems engineering this would be an analogue indication. However, it is also possible to provide digital indication, as shown in the figure, by using a counter, appropriately coupled to the handwheel shaft.

A simple extension to automatic operation is provided by using an electric motor to drive the hand wheel in response to remote electrical signals, normally through a reduction gear. This is represented in fig. 4.1–2. It is best to use this arrangement as an on/off control of actuation speed, which means that the electric motor has only three possible running states, full forward, stop and full reverse. The electric motor should stop quickly after breaking the circuit to avoid coasting, either by general friction or, preferably, by an

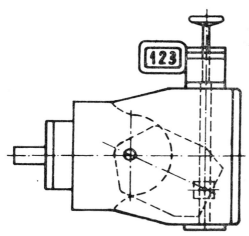

4.1–1 Hydrostatic unit controlled by handwheel with displacement indicator

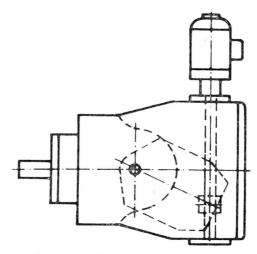

4.1–2 Hydrostatic unit with spindle driven by electric motor

electromagnetic mechanical brake. It is known that in order to avoid instability, there must be a dead zone in an automatic on-off controlled system, which should be larger than the coasting distance. This dead zone naturally limits the obtainable accuracy and speed of change of the displacement setting. The indication of displacement setting is either by the digital counter, or by potentiometer.

This arrangement is very suitable for not too high a spindle speed or rate of change of displacement nor when too exact a displacement control is required, because of the dead zone mentioned above.

For more rapid displacement setting, a force amplifier, normally consisting of a spool valve and follow-up piston is required. An example of this arrangement is shown in fig. 4.1–3 with servo-assisted manual follow-up control, as it could be used, for instance, on a vehicle.

One difficulty is to provide the pressure oil necessary to feed the force amplifier. In large installations it is normally possible to provide a special medium pressure circuit for this and other actuating requirements, although this is an objectional complication for small systems. Using delivery pressure has the disadvantage that this pressure is not always available as when there is no torque on the

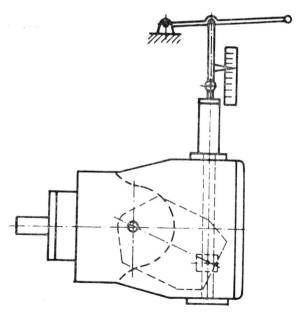

4.1–3 Hydrostatic unit, hand controlled with servo force amplifier

secondary shaft, whereas at other times pressure is inconveniently high. High pressures lead to excessive leakage of the spool valves and follow-up piston with consequent loss of efficiency, unless they are made to very high accuracy. An advantage is that both the force of the actuator and the force required to change the displacement of the hydrostatic unit are proportional to delivery pressure. With no delivery pressure the actuation force is very small, consisting only of friction of unloaded sliding surfaces and it is possible to actuate the pump by hand. This is often done by making the spool valve abut at the end of its travel on the follow-up piston or other suitable member so changing directly the position of the follow-up piston and the displacement setting. Some times it is possible to feed the actuator with

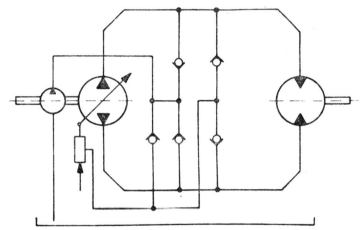

4.1–4 Circuit of transmission with servo control fed either by priming or main pressure through non-return valves

priming pressure, but this has the disadvantage that the priming pressure is fixed by other considerations and may involve the use of large follow-up pistons.

Another possibility with an externally primed hydrostatic transmission is to take the actuating pressure from several sources through non-return valves, possibly with an accumulator, as shown on fig. 4.1–4. Here the actuator is connected to both main lines and to the priming pressure line through non-return valves. Thus priming pressure is available as a minimum but as pressure builds up in the main system, more pressure becomes available for the actuator, at the same time as actuation becomes harder with increasing main pressure. Note that the decompression and relief valves are not shown in fig. 4.1–4.

All actuators described in this section require an external control
signal, e.g. by hand wheel, electrical impulses, etc. in accordance with
the requirements of the particular drive. In the next section actuators controlled by delivery pressure will be described.

Section 4.2 *Delivery pressure operated controls*

It is often preferable in practice to control hydrostatic units automatically by the delivery pressure. The hydrostatic unit with prime
mover and control then constitutes a small automatic hydraulic
pumping station. The control takes the form of a constant pressure or
constant power actuator.

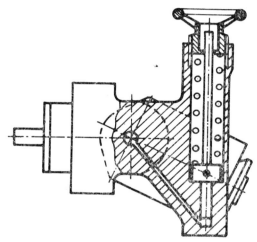

4.2–1 Scheme of constant pressure actuator on flange mounted hydrostatic
unit

A constant pressure actuator is shown schematically in fig. 4.2–1,
with a flange mounted hydrostatic unit. The arrangement is extremely simple, the delivery pressure acts on a piston which is spring loaded and linked to the actuation pivot of the hydrostatic unit. The
displacement is reduced when the pressure becomes greater than the
corresponding spring force on the area of the actuator piston. The
disadvantage of this simple scheme is that very strong springs are
required for the usual high pressures in hydrostatics. Furthermore, a
precise reduction of pump delivery at the set pressure requires a low
rated spring with a large preload. On careless disassembly of such an
actuator, the spring may expand suddenly, endangering health and

property. This accident is very aptly called some times "spring explosion."

The functional diagram of the hydrostatic units with the constant pressure actuator is shown in fig. 4.2–2. The position of the actuator changes the displacement setting, which in turn changes the flow delivered by the pumping unit. The pressure changes in consequence

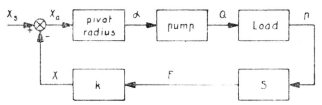

4.2–2 Functional diagram of hydrostatic unit with constant pressure actuator

of and in accordance with the properties of the load (fluid consumer) and varies the force on the actuator piston, which in turn determines through the spring constant, the position of the actuator piston.

It should be mentioned that the hydrostatic unit with a pressure operated actuator is an arrangement which can become unstable and produce violent oscillations. The conditions for the instability can be studied from the functional diagram, one member of which, namely the load or connection between flow and pressure is external and will not be known accurately at the time of manufacture. Indeed any disturbance will be amplified by the hydrostatic unit itself, which is a power amplifier operative by change of displacement setting and change of flow with the necessary energy supplied by the input shaft. The existence of oscillation then depends on whether the disturbance will be more attenuated around the loop (including reflection of a pressure wave from the load) than it is amplified in the hydrostatic unit.

In practice it is often necessary to put a calibrated restriction in the line to the actuator piston to avoid oscillation. Preferably this restriction is bypassed by a non-return valve, so that displacement can be rapidly reduced to avoid pressure surges, but increased only slowly.

Constant power actuators are very similar except that the actuator piston is loaded with several springs with different constants and different lengths in parallel, and the springs are now much stiffer. Referring to the graph of fig. 4.2–3, as soon as increasing pressure overcomes the preload of the longest spring, it is compressed in proportion to the pressure. After some reduction of displacement the

next spring abuts, against the actuator piston, causing a higher
effective spring constant and requiring a greater increase of pressure
for the same travel of actuator piston and reduction of delivery.
Further on the actuator piston strikes a fixed abutment, fixing the
delivery flow at a higher pressure. With further increase of pressure a
relief valve begins to blow preventing further increase. This constant
power control is also an unstable arrangement and the same remarks
and remedies apply as above.

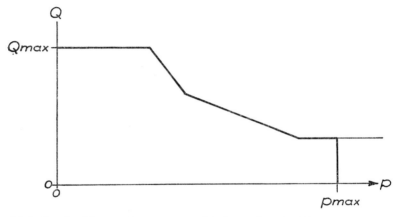

4.2-3 Graph of flow against pressure of hydrostatic unit with constant power
actuator

A hydrostatic unit equipped with a practical constant /power
actuator, as just described is shown in fig. 4.2–4. It is usual to put
not more than two springs in parallel, but it would be possible to use
more springs to give a closer approximation for the constant
power relation between pressure and delivery.

In order to avoid too heavy springs, one can pilot operate the
actuator piston, as shown in fig. 4.2–5. Here the spring behind the
actuator piston is very light since it only has to return the piston
when there is no pressure, and the relation between pressure and
delivery as described above is now given by a spring with variable
characteristics in the pilot valve.

A refinement is contained in fig. 4.2–5 in so much as with con-
tinued pressure rise the pilot valve piston opens a passage directly
to exhaust, after it has opened the passage admitting fluid to the
actuator piston for reducing delivery. The piston of the pilot valve
thus also acts as a relief valve. This again has the effect of improving
the dynamic response because the valve spool begins to travel some

4.2-4 Hydrostatic flange mounted unit with constant power actuator

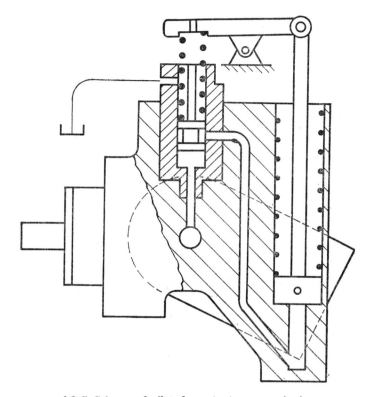

4.2–5 Scheme of piloted constant power actuator

time before the limiting pressure is reached, and thus opens a passage to exhaust with sudden rise of pressure much more quickly than would a separate relief valve.

Both the delivery pressure operated controls as described in this section are widely used in hydraulic presses and other hydraulic installations.

4.3 Combined control of transmission and prime mover

So far we have been concerned with hydrostatic transmission with a constant input speed used to produce a controlled variable output speed. It is however also possible and, in many cases desirable, particularly if the prime mover is an internal combustion engine, to also vary the primary speed in accordance with the speed and torque demand from the secondary shaft. Although these problems are a part of general mechanical engineering, and not strictly of hydrostatic transmission, they will be briefly discussed in this section because of their frequent occurence in the application of hydrostatic transmissions.

a) *Engine speed selection by governor*

To introduce the new concept, it is useful to imagine the hydrostatic transmission driven by an IC engine. There it will always be necessary to have a governor which in the case of a diesel engine

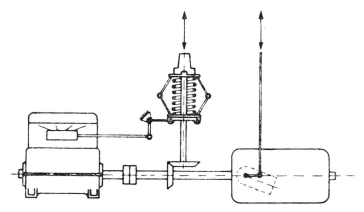

4.3–1 Scheme of hydrostatic drive with governed i.c. engine

reduces the fuel injection in order to avoid overspeed. Such an arrangement is schematically represented in fig. 4.3–1, using a governor with a fly ball speed sensing device. This sensing device, although known since the 18th century for windmills, is still frequently used despite its inherent non-linearity but other speed sensing devices such as small hydrostatic pumps working against a restrictor and electrical speed generators are available. Naturally the selected speed of the governor can be adjusted, as indicated by arrows in fig. 4.3–1.

The drive of fig. 4.3–1 consisting of governed engine and hydrostatic transmission can be influenced by two controls, namely the governor speed selection and the transmission setting α. For a certain speed selection the governor maintains this speed by changing the position of the fuel injection rack, which is practically proportional to the torque developed by the engine. When the power demanded

from the drive is reduced, it is possible to reduce the selected speed
of the engine, which will then be maintained by the governor at a
lower speed. Naturally it will then not be possible to produce full
output speed with primary control alone. If with reduced power,
full output speed should be required, it is possible to introduce
secondary control to increase the ratio of the hydrostatic transmission beyond 1:1, as described in section 3.1.

To prevent stalling of the engine by too large a torque on the
secondary shaft one more device will be required (fig. 4.3–2). Stalling
of the engine always begins by a loss of speed, and it is possible to

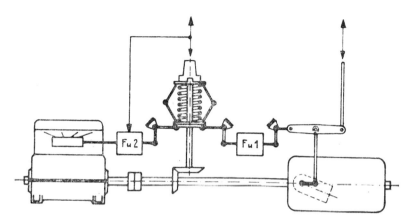

4.3–2 Drive with governor influencing both engine injection and transmission
control through functional losses

link the governor to the transmission control by an additional lever
through a small functional box (Fu 1) as shown in the figure. In
normal operation this functional box is inoperative, as two members
have play between, and engine speed is governed by injection. If
engine speed still has a tendency to fall when the fuel rack is at full
injection, the members of the functional box engage and operate the
lever reducing the primary displacement α. This reduces output
speed and also the torque required by the primary for a given pressure and secondary moment, which unloads the engine and allows it
to maintain its selected speed. In most cases it is desirable to interpose between the speed sensor and the transmission control lever
components such as force amplifiers, integrators and dashpots known
from the design of automatic speed governors to improve the trans-
ient performance.

For correctness, there is also shown in fig. 4.3–2 a functional box (Fu 2) between the governor and the fuel injection rack together with a connection which indicates that this functional box may be influenced by the speed selection of the governor. Here this functional box maintains the fuel injection rack in its position of maximum injection, allows the governor to travel further if the speed still falls and reduce the transmission ratio through the other functional box.

When the anti-stall device of fig. 4.3–2 is in operation the secondary speed is proportional to the speed control setting, as long as the secondary torque remains low. When this torque threatens to stall the engine, output speed is reduced by the anti-stall device just sufficiently to allow the engine to maintain its speed. The drive really is an automatic feed back control system controlling the engine speed, in the lower torque range by the injection, and when injection has reached its maximum value, by reducing the transmission ratio which reduces the torque load on the engine. It has all the advantages of feedback control and maintains the engine at its selected speed even if the engine torque no longer comes up to its specified performance. The engine speed can still be freely chosen by the speed selection of the governor.

b) *Load diagrams of IC engines*

For a proper study of the control possibilities of IC engines one should refer to the engine torque speed graph given in fig. 4.3–3. Without going into the details of diesel engine behaviour, the maximum power is developed at the point of maximum speed and maximum torque. When only reduced power is demanded, it would be possible either to reduce speed or to reduce torque. The torque developed by the engine for a given injector position has a slightly curved characteristic as shown by the thin continuous line, but for all practical purposes the torque can be considered proportional to injector position and independent of speed. While it is generally possible to reduce engine speed at full torque for reduced power output, it is not advisable to go too far, because at low speed, bearing loads and smoke become excessive. In consequence the region of favourable engine operation is limited to certain parts of the torque speed diagram, approximately as shown in fig. 4.3–3 by the heavy dotted line. According to this line full torque may be used from the maximum speed until some lower speed which is usually 33% to 40% of maximum speed. Still lower speeds may be used at low torque, according to the inclined part of the dotted line, which goes down to the lowest permissible idling speed. The remaining part of the dotted line limits the maximum engine speeds at any torque.

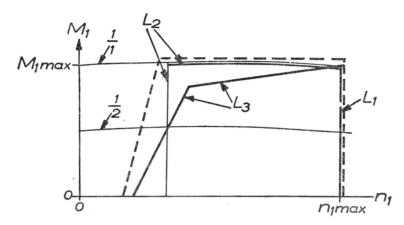

4.3-3 Torque-speed graph of i.c. engines with load lines

Within the limits given by the dotted line in fig. 4.3–3, the engine may be operated at any torque and speed combination. It is normal however, to always control the engine at certain combinations of torque and speed denoted by the lines L_1, L_2 and L_3. These lines are normally called load lines.

When the engine is governed at constant speed by variation of injection or torque, it is working on the load line L_1. This load line extends vertically downwards on the maximum power point, corresponding to reduced torque and constant speed. It should be mentioned, that sometimes the governor increases speed a little with reduced torque for stability. This is called "droop" and results in a slight incline of the vertical line, but it has no influence on the fundamental behaviour.

Another possibility of operation at reduced power is to maintain the maximum torque and to reduce speed, corresponding to the load line L_2. This is what is done in manual shift motor cars, when running with full throttle below maximum speed. Full throttle is not recommended at very low speeds here either, as the conditions are similar to the dotted line limit mentioned above. In order to reduce output power to zero, it is necessary to reduce the torque, as indicated by the load line L_2 which becomes vertical at low speed.

The best load line seems to be L_3, which reduces torque slightly and speed rapidly at the beginning of power reduction. Later the load line L_3 turns a corner and reduces torque only, in order to stay well within the dotted line limit. Just before the corner, this load line goes through the point of minimum fuel consumption. Naturally, the straight segments and the corner of the load line can be replaced by a suitably curved line.

An ideal control arrangement for the hydrostatic transmission would take the required power from the diesel engine according to the load line L_3 in order to produce the required secondary speed.

c) *Control of engine load*

A simple method for loading the engine approximately according to the load line L_3 is obtained by extension of the anti-stall device shown in fig. 4.3–2. As described, the device limits engine torque at full injection by controlling the transmission ratio when heavy secondary torque demands this. Now in order to produce load line L3, the functional box Fu2 between the governor and the injection pump can be used. This box is influenced by the speed selection of the governor in such a way that for each speed selection the engine speed is maintained by injection until at the desired maximum torque, as given by the load line, the functional box prevents further increase of injection. From thereon the engine is working at the selected speed and at the torque given by the load line, and its speed is automatically controlled by the transmission ratio.

It is instructive to represent the operation of the combined engine transmission control in a functional diagram as shown in fig. 4.3–4. The output of the governor proportional to the difference between selected and actual engine speed enters the functional boxes Fu 1 and Fu 2. The transmission ratio is equal to the difference between the position of the speed control lever and the output of Fu 1 and determines secondary speed and, as mentioned before, secondary torque. This torque reappears as the primary torque, depending on the transmission ratio as shown by the vertical cross connection. The output of the governor also enters the functional box Fu 2, which is influenced furthermore by the speed control lever. The output of this functional box is the position of the injection rack, which is proportional to the torque developed by the engine. Both this torque and the torque required by the transmission determines the engine speed, as shown by the left upper block.

Normally the system represented by this functional diagram is non-linear, but it becomes linear, except for the effect of the functional boxes, if the secondary torque is independent of speed, as occasionally happens in practice. In this case the primary torque becomes directly proportional to the transmission ratio.

The secondary torque speed characteristics of the control arrangement in fig. 4.3–4 are shown in fig. 4.3–5. Actually there are two

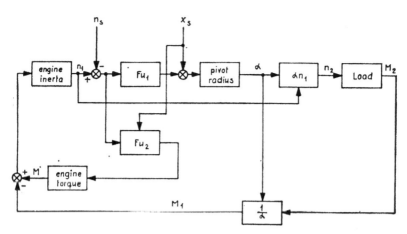

4.3-4 Functional diagram of combined engine and transmission control on load line

levers to adjust transmission output, namely the transmission control lever and the governor speed selector. The latter lever also changes the speed obtained from the transmission control lever, and the power limit of the transmission is shown by the power lines PI, PII, PIII in the figure. It can therefore be said, that secondary speed is proportional to the speed control position until, through increasing secondary torques, the power limit is reached. Both the constant of proportionality and the position of the power limit depend on the selected speed of the governor and on the load line. Strictly speaking, the engine is loaded on the load line L_3 when the transmission control is effective through the functional box Fu 1. At lower torques the engine runs at constant selected speed with less injection and lower engine torque.

The control arrangement described so far does not prevent over pressure in the hydrostatic transmission or continuous blowing of the relief valve. In order to achieve this, it is possible to introduce a pressure transducer which reduces transmission ratio on over pressure. This over-pressure limiting device is shown in the functional diagram, fig. 4.3–6, which is the same as the functional diagram, fig. 4.3–4 except for the addition of the pressure transducer. The transducer reduces the transmission ratio through another functional box Fu 3. The tranducer only acts when the pressure is getting too high and is inoperative with normal pressure, so acting rather like a relief valve but reducing load instead of blowing off. Naturally it is still recommended to fit relief valves because of pressure surges. The effect

9

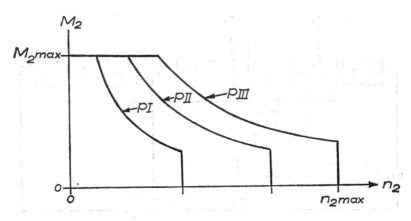

4.3–5 Secondary torque-speed graph of drive with combined engine and transmission control

of the pressure transducer can also be seen on the secondary torque speed diagram, fig. 4.3–5. There it limits the maximum secondary torque without changing the speed control lever or the action of relief valve. Sometimes it may be desirable for the limiting pressure of the pressure transducer to depend on the selected speed of the governor, giving somewhat smaller maximum pressure and torque with reduced power setting. This can be done very easily and is indicated by a connection entering the functional box Fu 3 from the speed selector.

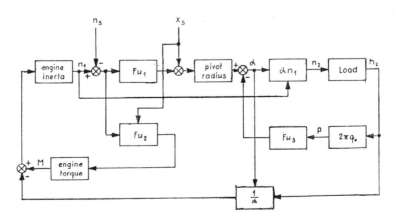

4.3–6 Functional diagram of combined engine and transmission control including pressure limiting device

The control arrangement shown schematically in fig. 4.3–2 and in the functional diagram, fig. 4.3–6, has many desirable characteristics and can be made simpler by omitting some links. It allows selection of the input power and running the IC engine on a desired load line with speed controlled by the speed control lever. Neither stalling nor over-speeding of the engine are possible, and the only difficulty may be finding the zero point as mentioned in section 4.5.

Sometimes it is desirable to have single lever control of the whole drive, which can be obtained by linking both governor speed selection and speed control lever. This however automatically reduces the flexibility of the arrangement in favour of simpler operation. It is not proposed to describe here the many variants of this scheme required to obtain special control characteristics and only two cases of practical importance will be mentioned.

The first special case is a very simple extension of the arrangement of fig. 4.3–1 having separate engine governing and transmission control. Now the speed selection of the governor is linked with the transmission control in such a way, that the engine is running slowly at low transmission ratio, and increases its speed with increasing transmission ratio. The combined control lever would therefore both increase the governor speed selection and the transmission control ratio when accelerating.

Another practical special case of the control scheme of fig. 4.3–2 is obtained by replacing the functional block Fu 1 with a direct link. Then the engine is always governed by changing the transmission ratio, and the functional box Fu 2 prevents the engine over-speeding. The output speed is now determined by changing the governor speed selection and zero secondary speed obtained by governing the speed so low that no output torque can be produced. This arrangement is practicable in some instances, especially for vehicle drives.

4.4 Servo Controls

a) *Hydrostatic transmission as part of feed back control system*

In the first part of this section the behaviour of a primary controlled hydrostatic transmission will be described, when it is used as a part of a larger feed-back control system, for example the speed control of a vehicle or positional control of a moving member.

Historically the position control of a heavy moving member was one of the first applications of hydrostatic transmission. Indeed it has been used to position the gun turrets of capital ships since the first years of this century.

In feed back control systems the secondary speed should be proportional to the displacement setting, but there are now two disturbing influences as will be explained with reference to the equivalent hydraulic circuit on fig. 4.4–1. The first influence is the leakage represented on the hydraulic circuit by bypass restrictors, giving a speed error proportional to secondary torque.

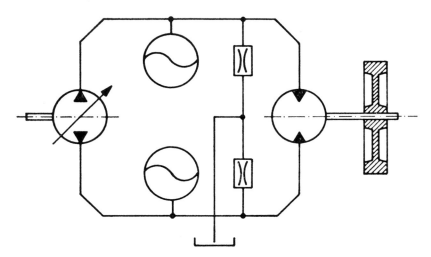

4.4–1 Equivalent circuit with accumulators and bypass restrictors simulating compressibility and leakage

The other effect, very important in position control systems loaded with large inertia, is due to the compressibility of the oil contained in the main system and other parts under the high pressure which varies with secondary torque. This is shown in fig. 4.4–1 by accumulators on both main lines. This means that the delivery from the primary can go into the accumulator to cause an increasing pressure instead of producing secondary speed.

In other words the inertia load can oscillate around its mean position (which moves with time), having as restraining agent the oil pressure and consequent energy which builds up in the accumulator due to the oscillation. As it is known that the frequency of oscillation is lowerer with pressure build up for a certain movement or with a larger capacity. The oscillation frequency is also lowered if the inertia on the secondary shaft increases.

The effect of this oscillation is that on rapid starting, the accumulator fills up with oil, producing torque gradually instead of instantly and so limits the attainable response to control signals.

The functional diagram illustrating the possibility of oscillation between the load inertia and the oil compressibility is shown in fig. 4.4–2. Compared to the functional diagrams of section 3.3, the

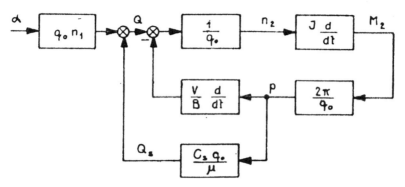

4.4–2 Functional diagram of transmission including compressibility and leakage

difference is that the flow, due to compressibility of the oil in the main system and other components external to the working cylinders of the hydrostatic units, is proportional to the volume of oil under variable high pressure and to the rate of change or time derivative of the pressure. This flow is deducted from the flow causing secondary speed. Numerically the capacity is given by the quantity of oil needed to cause a given pressure difference. The main contribution comes from the compressibility of the oil, proportional to the volume under variable pressure between primary and secondary, as represented in fig. 4.4–2. Other contributions come from the expansion of the main system and other members.

This functional diagram is an accurate representation of the transmission in fig. 1–4 loaded with a flywheel for testing purposes. The torque is proportional to the rate of change or derivative of the secondary speed, because the friction and windage losses of the flywheel are neglegible compared to the torque capabilities of the transmission. On the other hand with the dimensions of the flywheel as shown, it is possible to produce the full torque of the transmission with quite a slow change of secondary speed.

Some times one provides additional capacity by fitting actual accumulators. This always slows down response, but it will also

damp pressure surges due to improper manipulation or jerky movement of the transmission control.

The functional diagram, fig. 4.4–2 is also applicable for negative
values of speed, torque and pressure, if the latter is defined as difference of the absolute pressure in both main lines, as introduced in
section 3.1. It is now easy to determine, from the figure, the mathematical transfer function, as is done in any standard text book on
feedback control systems. (see Gille Bibliography 6).

It has been seen that the combination of load inertia and the elas-
ticity of the oil columns in the main system constitutes an oscillatory
system. It is damped by the leakage, and by any component of the
torque opposing secondary shaft movement, which increases linearly
with speed as for instance, viscous friction. In effect any such opposing torque diminishes the torque available to accelerate the load and
thus gives a damping effect. Accepting the power loss one can fix an
artificial viscous damper to the secondary shaft if the natural damping is not satisfactory. Furthermore any opposing torque increasing
more than linearly e.g. with the square of the secondary speed, also
contributes non-linear damping.

b) *Control properties of variable secondary with constant pressure*

As shown in section 3.1 when a variable secondary is supplied with
constant pressure, the shaft torque is very nearly proportional to the
displacement setting, which leads to acceleration control. This means
that the acceleration of the load is proportional to displacement setting. Consequently the acceleration of secondary shaft is independent
of the speed of the secondary shaft, which may lead to overspeeding
and which makes stabilizing of a large control system more difficult.
Therefore it may still be necessary to introduce an opposing torque
artificially, although there is no possibility of oscillation of the secondary shaft due to variable pressure columns of oil.

Instead of a friction damper on the secondary shaft with corresponding power loss, it is in many cases preferable to fit a tachometer
to the secondary shaft which reduces the displacement setting proportionally to speed. Since it reduces the torque available for acceleration of the load with increasing speed, it has a damping action exactly as a viscous friction damper on the shaft. This arrangement really
is a special case of tachometer feedback, frequently used for stabilisation in control system design. Instead of an electrical tachometer, it
is possible to use a hydraulic tachometer on the secondary shaft, for
example, a vane pump working against a suitable restrictor. The
pressure output of the hydraulic tachometer can be used to reduce

directly the secondary displacement through a small additional linkage. For proper stabilisation, it is essential for the tachometer to be operative for all possible speeds and in both directions.

Instead of a variable secondary, it may be preferable to use a fixed displacement secondary fed from a constant pressure source through an electrically controlled servo valve, shown in fig. 4.4–3. The advantage is the low power electric control signal and the disadvantage is the power wastage and pressure drop in servo valves.

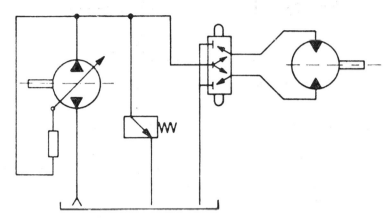

4.4 3   Circuit of constant secondary controlled by servovalve fed with constant pressure

Therefore this arrangement is usually limited to very small power requirements. The flow resistance of the servo-valve reduces pressure and torque on the secondary shaft with increasing speed, thus acting itself as a damper. Another advantage of the arrangement is a possibility of putting the servo valve near to the secondary, giving a small volume under variable pressure and consequent high rate of response.

c) *Differential actuated hydrostatic transmission*

One arrangement of special practical importance for servo position control should be mentioned and is represented in fig. 4.4–4. Here a spindle actuated primary is used. The spindle is equipped with a differential gear. One branch of this differential (corresponding to one axle in a motor car) is driven by the electric control motor as before, the other branch (corresponding to the other axle in a motor car) is driven in the opposing sense by the secondary shaft.

This makes a shaft connection necessary from the secondary shaft

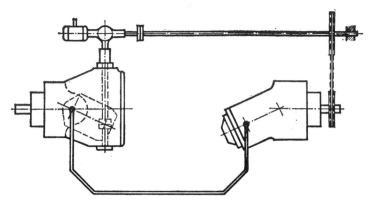

4.4–4 Hydrostatic transmission actuated through differential by electric
motor and secondary shaft

back to the primary control device. The body of the shaft differential
(corresponding to the universal joint shaft in motor cars) is connected
to the actuating spindle of the primary. If the electric motor turns
in response to control signal, with initially zero primary displacement
and zero secondary speed, a primary displacement is set, resulting
in a secondary shaft speed which, through the connecting shaft and
the differential, annuls the primary displacement. Thus one has a
position control system, because secondary shaft position follows the
position of the shaft of the electric control motor. The dynamic
aspects are as already described for the primary controlled hydrostatic transmission, in particular figs. 4.4–1 and 4.4–2 are applicable.
The gain of the control loop is adjusted by changing the diameter of
the chain wheels. Sometimes the connecting shaft between secondary
and primary is replaced by a so called electrical shaft or selsyn.

The differential actuated hydrostatic transmission is sometimes
used for winch drives, where the small electric motor is called a guide
motor. The friction on the guide motor shaft should be large enough
that for it to come to a certain stop in spite of the displacement setting forces reflected back through the differential. Under this condition the arrangement has the effect of definitely stopping the
secondary shaft even if it is under permanent torque as produced by
a suspended load. For fine control it is quite practicable to use a variable speed electric motor.

4.5 Special control problems

a) *Stopping of secondary shaft*

One problem of hydrostatic transmission arises from the fact that the secondary speed is very nearly independent of secondary torque. In consequence it may be difficult to assure a complete stop of the secondary shaft. It can be done obviously by setting the primary displacement very exactly to zero, but since there is nothing that can be perfect, creeping may occur which can be stopped only by leakage. With the normal small leakage, an error of the primary displacement of only 2% would produce the full torque M_{2dir} available at full speed. Therefore stopping by friction is problematical. The situation can be summarized in saying that the drive, of a vehicle, for example has a tendency to creep with inexact primary displacement setting, and this tendency to creep is very strong and cannot be overcome except by a very substantial torque.

One possibility which is sometimes used is a bypass valve between both main lines which is opened when primary setting is near zero usually by a follower and cam connected to the primary displacement setting. This has two disadvantages, namely that starting may be irregular depending on the closing characteristics of the bypass valve, and with open bypass valve no braking of the secondary shaft is available.

A better way is to feed back to the primary displacement the motion of a secondary shaft. A possible method is shown in fig. 4.5–1, which is generally similar to the arrangement of fig. 4.4–4. There is a chain drive and a special shaft connecting the secondary shaft to the primary. This shaft drives through a slipping clutch, a suspending nut on the primary displacement setting spindle that can move up and down with the nut between two abutments. If there is a small error in primary displacement setting around zero, the movement of the nut corresponding to any secondary movement reduces the primary displacement completely to zero. This happens only over a limited range, outside of which the nut goes against one of the abutments and the secondary shaft continues to rotate and the clutch slips.

The limiting factor of this arrangement is the power consumption of the slipping clutch, which must transmit enough torque to turn the suspending nut. It is possible to gear down the feed back shaft in order to reduce the torque to be transmitted by the slipping clutch. This is finally limited by the fact that, with large reduction ratios, the correction on the primary displacement takes effect very slowly, allowing the secondary shaft to travel some distance before

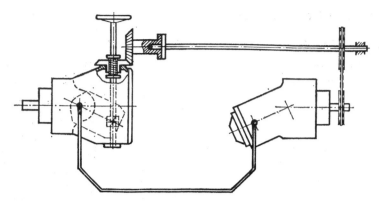

4.5–1 Stopping scheme for secondary shaft by connection to primary
displacement

coming to rest. In order to limit the torque consumption one should
provide real dry friction independent of speed, or better still a clutch
in which friction decreases with increasing speed and that is able
to withstand slip at high speeds indefinitely.

It may be possible to unload the clutch by providing centrifugal
weights which reduce the pressure between the sliding surfaces at
high rotative speed. The control action resulting from the feedback
of the secondary shaft position through a slipping clutch is represented on the graph fig. 4.5–2. It amounts to introducing an artificial
dead zone in the speed control around zero secondary shaft speed.
This is also maintained when external loads tend to keep the secondary shaft creeping as with a vehicle stopped on a gradient.

A simple method of stopping the secondary shaft is based on the
observation that many hydrostatic pumping units tend to reduce
their displacement setting with a force proportional to delivery
pressure. As shown in fig. 4.5–3, these forces, which depend on the
valving details can be supplemented by two small cylinders. Each
of the cylinders is pressurized from one of the lines. Furthermore
there is a small amount of play between the actuation pivot and
the control lever, denoted in the figure by a slot.

The cylinders tend to reduce the primary displacement as soon as
pressure develops in the forward side of the system until the actuation pivot abuts against the end of the slot. Should the secondary
start to drive in reverse, the small cylinders tilt the primary in the
other direction until the actuation piston abuts against the other
end of the slot. Thus there is effectively a dead zone between the
external parts of the transmission control and the primary displace-

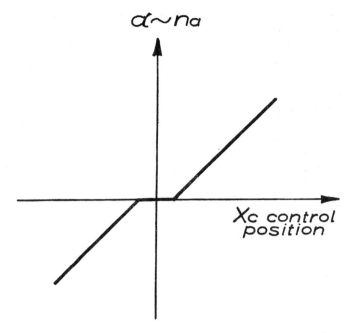

4.5–2 Graph of secondary speed against control lever position with stopping
scheme

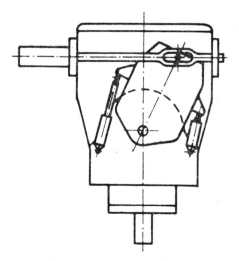

4.5–3 Stopping scheme with deliberate play in actuation of primary and small
cylinders reducing displacement with pressure

ment, and in consequence, the behaviour of the secondary speed is as shown in fig. 4.5–2, and the secondary shaft comes to a stop close to the position determined by the external transmission controls.

The disadvantage is that the dead zone is pressure dependent and not speed dependent as in the designs designed previously described. If the pressure should reverse while the secondary speed continuous in the forward sense, for instance because the load has to be braked, the displacement setting runs through the dead zone. This may give irregularities and shocks, which can be absorbed by fixing springs and dashpots to control the free motion in the slot between actuation pivot and transmission control. This simple stopping device is practical only when there is considerable friction on the secondary shaft, but it has the advantage of not requiring a mechanical connection back from the secondary shaft to the transmission control lever.

b) *Overspeed prevention of diesel engines*

When the hydrostatic drive is used to brake the output shaft, the power is returned to the prime mover by the motoring primary. With diesel engines this will result in overspeeding and damage to the engine in spite of the fuel injection being closed by the governor, as soon as the driving torque from the primary exceeds about 15% of the rated torque of the engine. This danger is especially likely with winch and hoist drives when lowering the load.

As an alternative to exhaust brakes hydraulic energy dissipators can be fitted. One form is a simple throttling valve, closed gradually by an engine overspeed signal, placed in one of the main lines. This

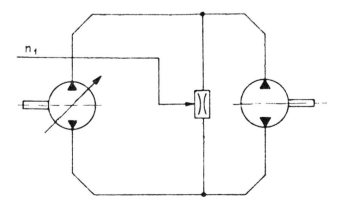

4.5–4 Circuit of transmission with bypass energy dissipator

valve produces on closing a pressure loss in the main flow and reduces the primary torque on the engine. The difficulty of this solution is that the throttling valve, must be large enough to pass the entire flow with a minimum of pressure loss during normal operation.

A better hydraulic energy dissipator is constituted by a throttling valve connecting both main lines as shown in fig. 4.5–4. With an overspeed signal from the engine, it bypasses a port of the flow. This does not directly reduce the system pressure nor the driving torque on the engine, but it dissipates some of the energy.

The operation of the bypass hydraulic energy dissipator is represented on the functional diagram, fig. 4.5–5. The first upper block represents a functional box opening the bypass valve only on overspeed of the primary or engine. The valve position causes some flow to be bypassed as shown by the next block, which reduces secondary speed. In accordance with the properties of the load, as represented

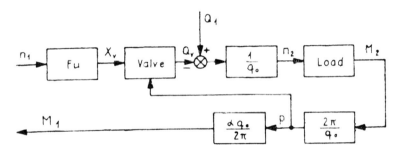

4.5–5 Functional diagram of bypass energy dissipator to avoid overspeed of prime mover

by the last upper block the secondary torque is reduced, which in turn reduces pressure and primary torque, as shown by the lower block. The reduced primary driving torque allows the engine to slow down.

The effectiveness of the bypass dissipator in reducing engine speed depends on the load characteristics and the torque speed relationship. If secondary torque is independent of secondary speed as in winch drives, the bypass merely increases secondary speed and is not effective in reducing primary torque. In that case it may be necessary to provide a link that reduces primary displacement at the same moment that the bypass valve opens, perhaps actuated by the valve flow itself. Such displacement reduction directly reduces the primary torque with a given system pressure. In this way also the speed fluctuation of the secondary due to the action of the bypass valve can be eliminated.

Finally it must be mentioned that the hydraulic energy dissipators produce an equivalent amount of heat in the hydraulic fluid. The cooling capacity of the hydrostatic transmission must therefore be dimensioned in accordance with the expected intensity of use of the hydraulic energy dissipator.

CHAPTER 5

HYDROSTATIC AND GEAR TRANSMISSION

5.1 *Combination of changespeed gearboxes with hydrostatic transmission*

For certain classes of application, as, for instance, spindle drives for lathes, the required speed range at constant power is so large that it is impractical from a size and efficiency point of view to try to produce the corresponding torque multiplication with a hydrostatic transmission alone. For machine tool spindle drives the required torque multiplication may be as high as 40, whilst in some multipurpose vehicles the required torque multiplication may exceed 10. Under such circumstances it is preferable to provide a changespeed gearbox between hydrostatic transmission and load. Consequently a part of the required torque multiplication is produced by changing gear.

The introduction of a changespeed gearbox seems contrary to the purpose of the infinitely variable hydrostatic transmission, but in practice, the gear ratio for the general range of speed is selected for the application and then fine control is effected by the hydrostatic transmission. The important thing is that a change of gear is never required during actual operation, and that the drive can be accelerated from rest in a high mechanical ratio. In the case of spindle drives for machine tools change of gear is only possible when the tool is not cutting. Hydrostatic transmissions with changespeed gearboxes are also used for multipurpose and off road vehicles, where selection of the lower gear ratio at the same time engages the front wheel drive for off road operation. Furthermore, electric main line locomotives can be designed more favourably if the required torque multiplication is not too high. Some such locomotives[1] are therefore equipped with two-step gear boxes between the electric motors and wheels, the gear ratio being changed for express or heavy goods trains.

The general lay out of a combined hydrostatic transmission and mechanical gearbox has no special problems, the only question is how to select the appropriate mechanical ratios. This is important with lathe spindle drives where a very large speed range is required. Generally it is desirable to provide some overlap of the constant

---

[1]The BB locomotives series **16 500** of the French Railway SNCF.

power speed range in view of the undesirability of changing gear under load.

A preferred selection of mechanical spindle speeds for a lathe is shown in fig. 5.1–1. The abscissa is the spindle speed in rpm, the ordinate the torque in arbitrary units, both on logarithmic scales which give the constant power hyperbola as a straight line. In this

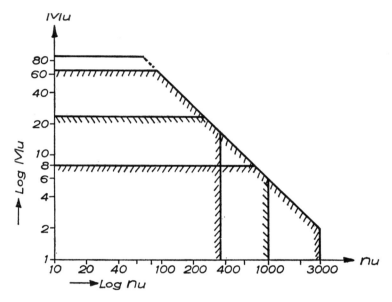

5.1–1 Torque-speed graph of hydrostatic transmission with 3 speed gearbox

example the full power speed range extends from 90–3 000 rpm. The top speeds of the spindle in the mechanical ratios are then selected as 3 000, 1 000 and 360 rpm leaving some overlap as shown. The overlap is desirable in order that full-power for turning is available for a certain range around the maximum speed of the ratios. Changing gear during cutting is impracticable because of the effect of the cut.

The use of the hydrostatic transmission gives a wide selection of cutting speeds at full power with simple three-speed gearbox. It furthermore allows faces to be turned with automatic control of the spindle speed so as to leave the cutting speed constant in spite of variation of the cutting radius. Some overlap is required on a general purpose machine to allow in the most unfavourable cases a wider range of spindle speed at full power without changing gear. Whilst hydrostatic transmission can be automatically speed controlled, the gearbox will usually be operated manually.

5.2 *Differential split power arrangement*

Whilst the preceding section was concerned with extension of the speed range of hydrostatic transmissions, there are many applications where the full speed range of the hydrostatic transmission, which normally goes from full forward to full reverse, is not needed. Indeed many applications require only a small variation around the nominal speed and it is there where the concept of power split can be used with best advantage.

The essential concept of split power hydrostatic transmission is the use of a gearbox or differential with two input and one output shafts. One of the input shafts is driven directly by the prime mover, the other one through the variable speed transmission and the gearbox output speed is the sum of both input speeds, as shown schematically in fig. 5.2–2. More often the output speed is a linear combination of both input speeds, obtained in some instances by adding reduction gears to the differential in the gearbox.

A differential gearbox as just described can be obtained by allowing the casing of a normal reduction gearbox to rotate. The speed of the output shaft is then the sum of the speeds of the casing and input shaft. In practice such gearboxes take the form of a differential gear similar to those used on motor cars, or of planetry gears. In this section the operation of a split power transmission will be examined in general terms while the wide variety of practical arrangements will be discussed in the next section. Referring first to the gearbox shown in fig. 5.2–1, the speed of the output shaft is a linear combination of the input speeds described quantitatively by the equation

$$n_u = \rho_i n_i + \rho_2 n_2 \qquad \qquad .. \quad (5.2\text{--}1)$$

In order to determine the torque relationship one imagines that first one input shaft is stopped and then applies the conservation of power between the other input shaft and the output shaft, neglecting losses. Repeat the process by supposing that the other input shaft is stopped, giving the equations:—

$$M_u = \frac{M_2}{\rho_2}; \quad M_u = \frac{M_{in}}{\rho_i} \qquad \qquad .. \quad (5.2\text{--}2)$$

The preceding equation implies that the torques of the two input shafts must have the relationship

10

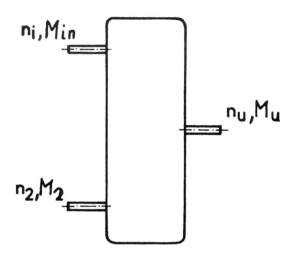

5.2-1 Scheme of differential gear box where output speed is a linear combination of the input speeds

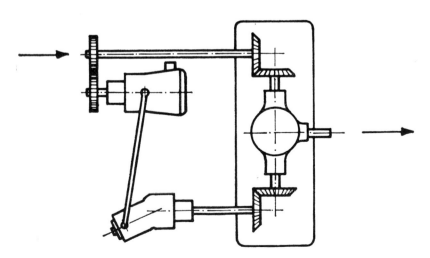

5.2-2 Scheme of simple split power hydrostatic transmission

$$\frac{M_2}{\rho_2} = \frac{M_{in}}{\rho_i} \qquad \text{..} \quad (5.2\text{-}3)$$

Equation (5.2–3) is the general equation of the equality of torque in the branch shafts of automobile differentials.

The split power transmission is obtained by coupling one input shaft of the differential gearbox and the hydrostatic primary to the prime mover, the other gearbox input shaft being driven by the secondary of the hydrostatic transmission whilst the output power is taken from the gearbox output shaft.

If the ratio ρ_2 defined by equation (5.2–1) is very small, implying that secondary speed has little influence on output speed, it is seen from equation 5.2–2 that the output torque is much larger than the secondary torque. Since secondary torque and speed are produced hydrostatically this makes it possible to use smaller hydrostatic units having lower cost, bulk and losses. As a corollary, with $\rho_2 \ll 1$ a change of secondary speed which may be produced with changing secondary torque through leakage and compressibility has a much smaller effect on output speed. It is possible to say that the torque is increased by $1/\rho_2$ but the absolute speed range decreased by ρ_2

The relations between the torques and speeds in equations (5.2–1) —(5.2–3) are an adequate representation of operation, but for completeness the power relationship will also be given. Combining equation (5.2–1) and the first part of (5.2–2) one obtains

$$P_u = 2\pi M_u n_u = 2\pi \left(\frac{\rho_i}{\rho_2} n_i M_2 + n_2 M_2 \right) \qquad \text{..} \quad (5.2\text{-}4)$$

The ratio between the total power transmitted to hydraulically transmitted power is given by

$$P_u/P_2 = 1 + \frac{\rho_i n_i}{\rho_2 n_2} \text{ since } P_2 = 2\pi n_2 M_2 \quad \text{..} \quad (5.2\text{-}5)$$

As is seen from equation (5.2–5) the power ratio is larger, the smaller the factor $\rho_2 n_2$ in the denominator. The discussion so far has been perfectly general, independent of the detail design of the differential gearbox, as long as its efficiency losses can be neglected. It should be noted that both speed and torque may become negative.

For a study of the speed ranges which can be obtained we refer to the schematic arrangement in fig. 5.2–2. The differential gearbox

is of the automobile type. One branch shaft of the differential is
connected to the transmission input, the other branch shaft to the
hydrostatic secondary and the main shaft is connected to the output.
The primary is driven through a pair of gears with the ratio $\rho_1 =
n_i/n_1$, and the other reduction factors ρ of equation (5.2–1) can be
contained in the bevel gears shown schematically on the figure.

The output speed is then, with the hydrostatic speed ratio a

$$\frac{n_u}{n_i} = \rho_i + a\frac{\rho_2}{\rho_1} \qquad \text{.. (5.2–6)}$$

If in the fig. 5.2–2 both the gears driving the primary and the
bevel gear have the same number of teeth, the factors ρ_i and ρ_2
become equal to 1:2 and equation (5.2–6) simplifies to

$$\frac{n_u}{n_i} = \frac{1+a}{2} \qquad \text{.. (5.2–7)}$$

It can be seen from the preceding equation that with the hydrostatic transmission driving full forward, $a=1$, the total speed range
is equal to unity. With the hydrostatic transmission stopped,
$a=$zero, total speed ratio is equal to one half, and with the hydrostatic transmission driving fully in reverse $a=-1$, the effective
speed ratio is zero. Reverse output speed can be obtained only by
having a hydrostatic transmission with a reverse ratio of greater
that 1:1 which can be accomplished by secondary control. The
hydrostatic torque is always equal to one half the output torque
even when the secondary is stopped. In this case the hydrostatically
transmitted power is zero, because the secondary speed is zero, but
but not the secondary torque. In other words, the hydrostatic
transmission is stationary under load and is subject only to leakage
losses.

The fundamental scheme discussed in this section embraces most
possible split power drives irrespective of their implementation. Such
drives are especially advantageous in drives requiring adjustment of
output speed for only a few per cent around their nominal value.
Then the factor ρ_2 of equation (5.2–1) can be very small, and in consequence the torque transmitted hydrostatically becomes small compared to the output torque. Also the influence of the slip of the
hydrostatic transmission in response to variation of torque is reduced
by the split power arrangement, depending on the ρ factors, leading
to an output speed of the split power drive still more independent of
output torque. This can be important in some applications. Quan-

titatively it can be got from equation (5.2–6), by allowing a to be variable with applied torque.

A possible variation of split power transmission is to exchange the input and output shafts. This is only practicable to give a constant output speed from a variable input speed, as will be described in section 6.4. In this variation all the equations developed remain valid, including the ratio between hydraulically and total transmitted power.

Section 5.3 *Practical schemes for split power*

The split power hydrostatic drive uses a differential gearbox, where the output speed is a linear combination of both input speeds to the gear box. The practical implementation can take a wide variety of forms. One well known form of the gearbox is the automotive differential. In this case the main shaft of the differential is usually coupled to the output, one branch to the prime mover, and the other branch to the secondary of the hydrostatic transmission whilst the primary is driven through a reduction gear from the input shaft. One example is shown in fig. 5.3–1, using a bevel gear reduction of about

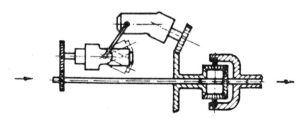

5.3–1 Split power transmission with bevel gears

1:3 between secondary and differential. In this case only one sixth of the output torque is transmitted hydrostatically.

It is also possible to use planetary gears as shown in fig. 5.3–2 using two primaries and two secondaries in parallel. This arrangement gives a very compact design, fitting neatly into the disc shape of a planetary gear, and eminently suitable for vehicle application.

There also exist split power hydrostatic drives which do not use gears. Just as a differential gearbox can be obtained from an ordinary one by rotating the casing, the gearless split power transmission is made by revolving the casing of the hydrostatic transmission. For this it is necessary to have primary and secondary in one casing suspended in bearings in which it can rotate.

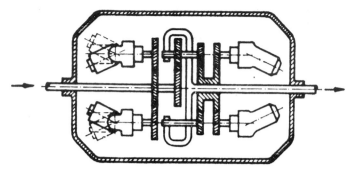

5.3-2 Split power transmission with planetary gears

The most practical arrangement for a gearless split power transmission is shown schematically in fig. 5.3–3. Here the casing is coupled to the input shaft, the primary shaft is prevented from rotating and the output is from the secondary shaft. It should be noted that the primary is located on the right and secondary on the left side of the figure. The output shaft from the secondary must pass through the hollow primary shaft.

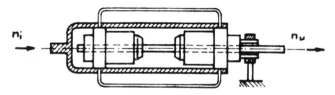

5.3-3 Gearless split power transmission

For the analysis, n_1 and n_2 denote the speeds of the primary and secondary shafts relative to the casing, n_i the input speed and n_u the true output speed.

From the kinematics of fig. 5.3–3 one obtains

$$n_2 = -n_u + n_i \; ; \; n_1 = -n_i$$

This gives

$$n_u = (1 + a) n_i \text{ since } n_2 + a n_1 \qquad .. \quad (5.3\text{–}1)$$

As shown by the preceding equation the gearless split power behaves similarly to one with a differential gear, only the maximum output speed is double the input speed, obtained with $a = 1$.

With the hydrostatic transmission stopped, output speed is equal to input speed, and with the hydrostatic transmission set to full reverse, the output shaft remains stationary.

Although this split power transmission has the advantage of being gearless it is beset with considerable difficulties. Not only must the primary hydrostatic unit have a centre hole large enough to pass an output shaft large enough for the apparent output power, but also the hydrostatic unit rotating with the full input speed poses a difficult balancing problem. Bent axis hydrostatic units are therefore unsuitable. Finally the difficulty of fitting the transmission control lever and the priming circuit in the rotating transmission limits the applicability of the gearless split power transmission. Nevertheless it has been used in practice.

Summarising the properties of split power transmissions; they are most advantageous if the required output speed range is small, because then only a small part of the output torque has to be produced hydrostatically. They all have the disadvantage of requiring a shaft connection between input and output. The final choice between split power and direct transmission depends on the relative cost and bulk of the hydrostatic units and the differential gears.

There also exist double differential split power transmissions, where the gearboxes possess four shafts, the speed of each being a linear combination of the other shaft speeds. One shaft is then connected to the input, two others to primary and secondary respectively, and the fourth shaft to the output. The gearbox may consist of two suitably connected automobile differentials, or of a planetary gear, where each planet has two gears meshing with different diameter sun gears, in addition to the annular gear meshing with one planet gear.

There are many possible configurations, and it is possible to compress the speed range obtained from the hydrostatic transmission with full primary and secondary control into a desired output speed range. This allows some saving in the hydrostatic power, but needs many more shafts.

The practical importance of the double differential split power transmission is too small to justify treatment here. A word of caution; when adapting such a transmission it is necessary to check that through the entire range nowhere in the many shafts are excessive values of torque or speed produced.

CHAPTER 6

PROBLEMS RELATED TO APPLICATIONS

6.1 Vehicle drives

a) *Wheel vehicles*

One important application of hydrostatic transmission is for vehicles powered by IC engines. Since vehicles have been used as an example throughout this book the treatment of wheeled vehicles can be brief. IC engines have characteristics which make hydrostatic transmission specially advantageous, since they cannot pull below a certain speed, and if accidentally slowed down they will stall. With vehicles running in either direction, all four driving states, namely forward driving, forward braking, reverse driving and reverse braking are used. For vehicles working on gradients dynamic braking with power feedback to the engine is a great advantage, not only as an additional brake, but also to relieve the load on the friction brakes.

Because hydrostatic transmission can give a secondary speed independent of torque, except for leakage, it helps to improve adhesion both on rails and on roads. It comes from the fact that with any wheel slip torque falls instantly with only a slight increase in speed, preventing the slipping wheel from accelerating as would be the case with a constant torque drive. If, for control reasons, a constant torque characteristic is preferable and produced by a suitable accessory, its action can be delayed so as to retain the constant speed characteristic for a short while. This is done by ensuring that on wheel slip the torque falls instantly and the accessory restoring the torque by increasing the displacement of the primary only acts slowly.

Vehicles with hydraulic or mechanical differential between two wheels are much less favourable for adhesion, because of torque equalisation in the differential. Many commercial limited slip differentials exist but it should be mentioned that two separate hydrostatic transmissions, one to each wheel, often make a very suitable limited slip drive. The admissible slip is governed by the leakage of the transmission, but additional slip can be introduced by parallel connection of both transmissions through a suitable restrictor. Still better results can be achieved by using a flow control valve between

both transmissions to allow for equalisation of flow independent of
pressure or torque differences.

b) *Tracked vehicles*

Tracked or crawler vehicles are specially suitable for hydrostatic
drive, because steering is effected by imparting different speeds to the
right and left track, and not by turning the wheels as in normal
wheeled vehicles. The simplest arrangement, shown in fig. 6.1–1, uses
separate hydrostatic transmissions for the right and left hand tracks.

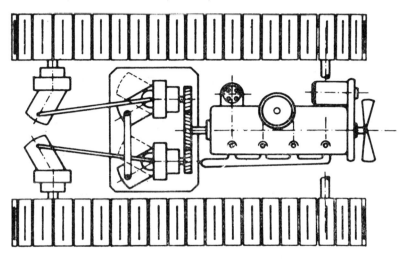

6.1–1 Scheme of a crawler tractor with transmission on both sides

The difference in speed setting gives different speeds to the tracks
causing the vehicle to turn. Since the transmission ratio of both
hydrostatic transmissions is independent of the applied torque, the
vehicle turns unaffected by torque variations which may be caused
by changes in the surface. This property is most important in order
to allow tracked vehicles to run safely with high speeds.

One point to note is that the difference in setting of the right and
left hand transmissions gives the difference in track speed, which is
proportional to the angular velocity of turning. If this difference is
set by a steering wheel, the angular velocity of turning is proportional
to the steering wheel position independent of road speed, resulting in
a much larger turning radius for a given steering wheel position at
high speeds. In order to obtain a turning radius or, strictly, a curve

proportional to steering wheeled position and independent of road speed, (as in wheeled vehicles) special devices are necessary. One such device would use a multiplication linkage to increase the difference of speed setting of the hydrostatic transmission for a given position of the steering wheel at high road speeds. Naturally this constitutes an undesirable complication.

An alternative arrangement, shown in fig. 6.1–2, uses two separate hydrostatic transmissions. The main hydrostatic transmission has a primary driven by the engine and two secondaries hydraulically in

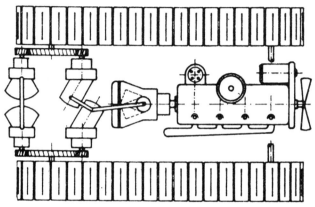

6.1–2 Scheme of crawler tractor with separate steering and main transmission

parallel for differential action coupled through reduction gears to each track. The torques supplied by the secondaries of the main transmission are thus equal, and the speeds of the tracks are variable consequent upon the differential action. In order to set the track speeds individually a second hydrostatic transmission is provided linking both tracks or side shafts and imposing a certain speed ratio depending on its setting. If this steering transmission is set with a 1:1 ratio, both tracks have equal speeds and the vehicle runs straight. By reducing the speed setting of the left hand unit of the steering transmission, the left track runs faster, both because the steering unit supplies driving torque and also because of the braking torque exerted by the right hand unit of the steering transmission on its track. The extreme case is given when the left displacement setting is zero, making the right track stationary. The vehicle then turns around its right track with its left track driving. Reducing the displacement setting of the hydrostatic steering unit on the other track the vehicle will turn in the reverse sense.

For a quantitative description of the operation of a tracked vehicle using a main and steering transmission refer to the functional diagram in fig. 6.1–3, which is similar to the diagram fig. 3.1–4 with two secondaries in parallel. As before, n_{2a} and M_{2a} denote the speed and torque of the left hand track and n_{2b} and M_{2b} denote the speed and torque of the right hand track, and the tetter M_2 represents the torque of each of the secondaries of the main transmission.

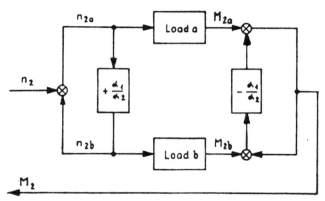

6.1–3 Functional diagram of crawler steering transmission

The difference in the track speeds is now adjusted by the steering transmission, as shown by the left vertical block containing the transmission speed ratio. The two blocks in the middle of the diagram represent the torque appearing on the side shafts in response to the track speed. Due to the differential action of the main transmission, the torque supplied by both main secondaries is equal, and the difference in track torque is produced by the steering transmission, as shown by the vertical block on the right hand side. Since this block connects track (b) to track (a) the relationship between torques is $-a_1/a_2$. The minus sign is introduced because one hydrostatic unit of the steering transmission is braking and the other unit is driving the other track. From this functional diagram the algebraic relations can easily be determined.

For proper steering the displacement of both steering units must be variable from zero to one. However, negative displacement of either steering unit is not needed and should be avoided, because of excessive torque development, which may go as far as to render the transmission self-locking. Since the speed ratio of the tracks imposed by the steering transmission is independent of the road speed, neglecting leakage, the turning radius is also independent making the multiplication linkage mentioned before unnecessary. A further advantage of this design is that linkages become comparatively simple, since the functions of the transmissions are strictly separated, one selecting vehicle speed, the other the turning radius.

A final word of caution; tracked vehicles are subjected to very rough handling, and the drive members must be dimensioned very generously. With some types of terrain the actual translation force exerted by the track can reach as much as 150% of the weight it carries, with correspondingly high loads on the transmission.

6.2 Propeller drives

a) *Hydrostatic propeller drives*

The driving of propellers by hydrostatic units is frequently contemplated, especially for ship propellers and ventilating fans and the problems particular to this application will be treated briefly in this section.

Hydrostatic variable speed propeller drives are an alternative to constant speed variable pitch propellers. Both are suitable for imparting a controlled amount of energy to the slip stream. An advantage of hydrostatic propeller drive is that the shaft to the engine is replaced by pipes and that the friction and leakage characteristics of the hydrostatic transmission effectively damp torsional oscillations. In essence, the hydrostatic transmission not only has the task of varying and controlling the propeller shaft speed, but also of transporting the energy over moderate distances from one or several engines to the appropriate propeller shaft.

Hydrostatic propellers on ships of seagoing size seem to be especially attractive, if they can be supplied by several comparatively small power packs comprising an engine and a variable primary. A typical example are 10 diesel power packs of 1 000 HP each to produce 9 000 shaft horse power through one or several hydrostatic secondary units. Not only can each power pack be made small enough to allow of removal through hatches for overhaul and replacement, but some engines can be stopped for slow speed. Furthermore, when top speed is not required, engines can be used for other duties, e.g. powering hydraulic winches or other machinery. So far the main obstacles seem to be the commercial availability of large hydrostatic units, but the author sees no technical difficulty to the production of hydrostatic units up to several thousand HP each, with reliability and other characteristics suited to marine service. Generally hydrostatic transmission is most appropriate for marine

service and the adaption of hydraulics is a fascinating part of
marine engineering.

For the quantitative adaption of the hydrostatic transmission
to a propeller drive the prime considerations are the torque and speed
of the propeller. As is well known, the propeller shaft torque increases proportionally to the square of the shaft speed, while the
constant of proportionality will depend on the flow characteristics
around the propeller. For ship propellers for instance this depends
on whether the ship is running light or loaded or towing some other
ship.

For a given condition of the ship, the highest shaft torque is needed at the highest shaft speed. Therefore the torque multiplication γ
as introduced in section 2.2 is equal to one and the apparent power
equal to the engine power of the drive. The quantitative aspect is
simple since from the maximum shaft horse power required a transmission working at a suitable pressure is selected which can supply
the power with the required life and reliability, usually very high in
marine service. The necessary reduction ratio is determined from the
speeds of the propeller shaft and the hydrostatic unit.

b) *Hydrostatic couplings as propeller drives*

Since the torque multiplication in a propeller drive is equal to
one, the speed range is comparatively low. In consequence, for small
powers propeller shaft speed can be varied by bypassing part of the
flow through an adjustable restrictor, as described in the first part of
section 3.1. This method is used for driving the cooling fans of diesel
engines radiators. The hydraulic circuit is shown in fig. 6.2–1. The
bleed restrictor is automatically controlled by a thermostat, in the
cooling water. The hydrostatic transmission acts as a thermostatically controlled coupling and replaces both bevel gear and shafts.

The efficiency of the arrangement in fig. 6.2–1 is poor as shown
in fig. 6.2–2 by the dotted line I. Since it is a coupling the efficiency
is equal to unity at full output speed when the bypass is closed,
and falls proportionally with decreasing output speed. Furthermore,
the line represents only the slip losses of a variable speed coupling,
to which must be added the hydrostatic transmission losses to give
the actual efficiency. This coupling is only feasible, from an efficiency
point of view, because the shaft torque falls sharply with decreasing
shaft speed, because of the propeller characteristics. Therefore the
energy loss, expressed as a percentage of full power, is not excess-
ively high. The power lost in couplings due to slip is always equal to
slipping speed multiplied by transmitted torque.

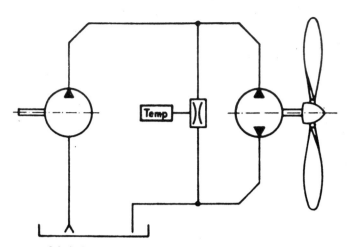

6.2-1 Circuit of propeller drive with bypass control

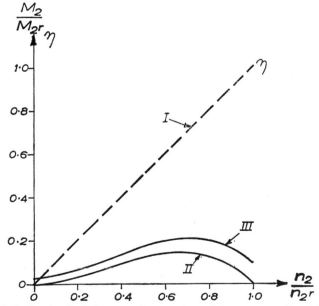

6.2-2 Graph of efficiency and power loss of bypass propeller drive

For a quantitative treatment the highest torque and speed of the propeller drive should be used as reference values. Then the propeller characteristics can be expressed as

$$\frac{M_2}{M_{2r}} = \left(\frac{n_2}{n_{2r}}\right)^2 \qquad \text{..} \qquad (6.2\text{--}1)$$

Neglecting the losses in the hydrostatic transmission units, one obtains the power loss as a function of shaft speed by multiplication of equation (6.2–1) with the slip speed and division by the reference speed

$$\frac{P_2}{P_r} = \left(1 - \frac{n_2}{n_{2r}}\right)\left(\frac{n_2}{n_{2r}}\right)^2 \qquad \text{..} \qquad (6.2\text{--}2)$$

where $\qquad\qquad P_r = 2\pi\, n_{2r}\, M_{2r}$

Equation (6.2–2) is represented graphically in fig. 6.2–1 by the line II. It is seen that the maximum power due to slip loss occurs between 60 and 70% of maximum speed and is equal to 15% of maximum power.

The line III on fig. 6.2–2 shows the power loss relative to the maximum power taking into account the transmission losses. The transmission losses have been calculated taking the examples of the different loss moments given in section 1.2–c. It is now seen that the highest power loss is about 21%, occurring at about two-thirds maximum speed.

In view of this poor efficiency, a variable primary, thermostatically controlled, would seem to be a much more elegant solution. The power loss of such a primary controlled propeller transmission at partial power, is somewhat smaller than the difference between curves II and III of fig. 6.2–2, mainly because the reduction of primary flow losses with low shaft speed. Finally it should be mentioned, that in curve III the flow losses in the restrictor of the bypass hydrostatic transmission are not included. They will lead to somewhat higher power loss at very low shaft speed, and perhaps prevent the propeller stopping completely.

A method of making the hydrostatic coupling more acceptable is to use a thermostatic valve that has only two positions, namely completely open and completely closed. This is then an on-off controller, which is acceptable due to the thermal inertia of the engine. An advantage of the hydrostatic coupling is that the valve, unlike a friction clutch, can be opened and closed frequently without ill effects while the detail design of the valve ensures smooth acceleration of the fan.

c) *Speed and power of ships' propellers*

In this part the relationship between the shaft speed, torque and power of ships' propellers will be considered. Whilst the torque is proportional to the square of shaft speed, the proportionality depends on whether the ship is running light or loaded, or the case of a tug, towing a large ship. In all these cases the shaft torque is higher than when running light, but it remains proportional to the square of the shaft speed. Fig. 6.2–3, two different examples of torque speed curves are shown, the lower one when running light and the upper one when towing.

Internal combustion engines develop a torque nearly independent of speed. If for the highest speed with a light ship the torque and speed of the engine are selected to match the torque curve of the ship at the point I the entire engine power can be transmitted to the shaft. If the ship is towing, the shaft torque follows the upper curve and with the available engine torque the shaft runs at reduced speed, as shown by the point II. Thus the engine runs at reduced speed and full torque, and therefore at reduced power; in the example about 82%.

Whilst running at reduced speed with full torque is permissible with small engines, for some large engines in may be necessary to reduce the torque in order to avoid too high a cylinder head temperature, which leads to a further reduction of the power supplied to the

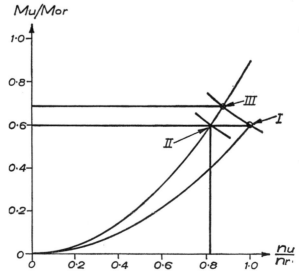

6.2–3 Propeller shaft torque against speed for ship running light and towing

propeller shaft. Such reduced torque is equivalent to the use of the upper part of the load line L 3 of section 4.3, which shows the reduction of the power available from the engine. If, on the other hand, engine and propeller shaft are matched for full power transmission for the towing ship, only a proportion of the engine power can be developed when running light because the propeller shaft requires lower torque at the highest admissible engine speed.

By the introduction of a variable speed transmission the propeller shaft speed can be reduced when towing whilst the shaft torque can be increased and the engine speed maintained constant. This means, that the torque speed point travels up on the constant power line of fig. 6.2–3, until point III, where full engine power is available at the shaft at somewhat reduced speed. This gives both high service speed and maximum pull and allows the engine to work at optimum power. In essence, the hydrostatic transmission adapts the engine to the shaft characteristics when both running light or towing.

This application requires a relatively small shaft speed range, in this example about 20% of maximum speed. From this point of view a split power split drive as treated in section 5.2 and 5.3 is indicated.

In fairness it must be said, that these requirements can also be obtained with other types of variable speed transmission and with variable pitch propellers running with constant shaft speed.

d) *Other application of hydrostatic propeller drives*

Hydrostatic propeller drives can be used with advantage in marine engineering in several ways for increasing the manoeuvrability of ships. Its advantages are the small size of a hydraulic motor and it being less susceptible to damage by water infiltration than an electric drive. One possible application for hydrostatic propeller drives is the so called "rudder propeller" for increasing side thrust at the stern of the ship.

Another such application, already done by electrically driven propellers on large ships, is to build a transversal tunnel in the bow equipped with a hydrostatic propeller, suspended in a pod not unlike an aircraft engine. This is shown schematically in fig. 6.2–4, where the small hydrostatic unit makes it possible to reduce dimensions and drag of the pod. The transverse tunnel with a propeller rotating in either direction, allows side thrust to be applied at the bow to assist turning, especially at low speed and is sometimes called "a bow thruster". Again, when the "bow thruster" is not needed for manoeuvring, the hydrostatic transmission primary can be used for other duties, as, for instance, assisting the main propeller drive or driving winches.

11

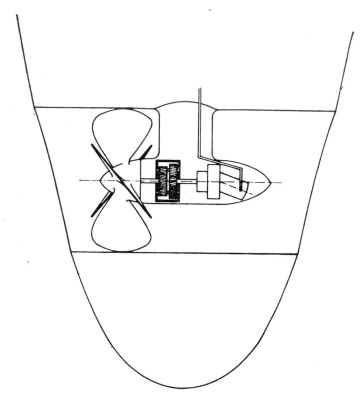

6.2–4 Scheme of bow tunnel with hydrostatic propeller drive

6.3 *Winch drives*

Winch and hoist drives are ideal applications of hydrostatic transmission due to the frequent stopping and starting under full load. In addition the fine speed control independent of secondary torque, which is a feature of hydrostatic transmissions, facilitates manipulation of suspended loads.

Winch drives can take many different forms, including hoists, windlasses, cranes and passenger or cargo lifts. The common characteristic is that output torque is mainly due to gravity and is independent of the speed, while it may vary widely with different loads. Furthermore, changes in the winding radius on cable drums will give different secondary torque requirements. High torque is required only in one direction, when hauling the cable in, whilst for releasing, only the torque to overcome the drum friction is required, thus simplifying the hydraulic circuit.

Winches and cranes are potentially dangerous, and must be equipped with suitable safety devices, mainly to give protection in the event of pipe breakages or loss of pressure due to other causes.

A typical hydraulic winch circuit, as shown in fig. 6.3–1, is the normal externally primed circuit treated in section 3.2, except that no decompression valve is fitted, since substantial torque is required only in one direction. The priming pressure is set by the relief valve shown, which also limits the pressure in the main return circuit. It must be sufficiently high to allow reverse rotation of the drum when releasing the cable.

Shown also in fig. 6.3–1 is a safety brake on the secondary shaft, normally applied by a spring, and released by a piston operated by the priming pressure. If breakage should occur, priming pressure would disappear and the brake be applied by the spring.

The speed selection during normal operation is done manually through the left hand actuator. The right hand actuator is controlled by the pressure in the upper main line and limits this pressure by reducing primary displacement when needed. The right hand actuator can be controlled by an external signal as indicated by the additional line. As an example, this signal could be proportional to the winding radius of a drum, allowing this actuator to keep the cable tension constant. Another signal sometimes used is the position of the boom of a crane which causes the actuator to limit the tilting

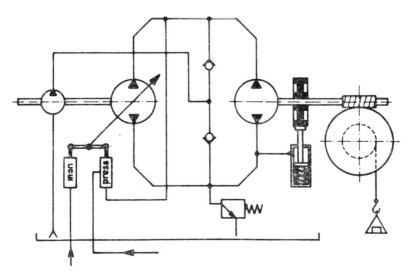

6.3–1 Circuit of hydrostatic winch drive with safety brake operated by priming pressure

12

moment on the crane structure, as given by the product of boom inclination and system pressure. This system avoids tipping accidents, especially important with high tower cranes.

When releasing the cable, the secondary acts as motor driven by the cable drum and supplies energy back to the primary and the shaft of the prime mover. It is necessary to provide sufficient braking capacity at the prime mover and perhaps introduce an energy dissipator as described in section 4.5. With an electric AC induction motor sufficient braking capacity is available, but if the electricity supply fails or the fuses blow, the braking torque of the motor disappears and it may run away. If the priming pump is driven by the same shaft, priming pressure may continue to be sufficiently high to hold the safety brake off (fig. 6.3–1). It will therefore be necessary to fit an electromagnetically controlled safety brake or equivalent device.

6.4 *Constant speed hydrostatic drives*

Whilst normally a hydrostatic transmission produces a controlled variable output speed from a nearly constant input speed, another interesting application is production of a constant output speed from variable input speed. The output speed is automatically kept constant, independently of input speed, so that the constant output speed hydrostatic drive constitutes a complete automatic control system, and not only an element of such a system as most hydrostatic transmissions.

Typical applications are alternator and refrigerator drives from road vehicle and air craft engines and gas turbines.

The quantitative analysis is exactly the inverse to the normal transmission as treated in section 3.1. Particularly, the torque multiplication is determined as the ratio of the speeds of the prime mover when the drive has to supply the same secondary speed. Since the secondary torque is necessarily constant with constant speed, this speed range is that at which constant power has to be supplied by the transmission. As mentioned before torque multiplication is limited to about 1:4, which is ample for gas turbines, but not excessive for lorry engines. In other words it is difficult to produce constant output speed from too low an input speed—with engine idling or running very slowly—because of the high speed multiplication required between input and output shaft. The desired torque multiplication together with the output power of the drive determines the apparent power, which governs the selection of the hydrostatic unit. (See section 3.1).

Since the speed range cannot include zero input speed, there is no imperative reason to use secondary control, corresponding to the primary control which is absolutely necessary in a normal hydrostatic transmission for zero output speed. In a constant speed drive with secondary control both flow and pressure are variable, while primary control gives constant flow and pressure, and is therefore preferable.

For automatic control of output speed it is necessary to use a feedback loop, comparing the actual output speed to desired output speed and correcting the transmission ratio accordingly. If the input speed is also measureable, it is recommended that a feed forward loop is also applied. This is shown in the circuit in fig. 6.4–1 with tachometers on input and output shafts which measure both speeds and control the primary displacement through the actuator shown as a box. In this circuit, the tachometers are vane pumps working against restrictors, which supply pressure signals to the actuator. Naturally electric tachometers are also suitable.

As shown in functional diagram fig. 6.4–2, the feed forward loop consists of an input-shaft tachometer, which controls the transmission ratio. Strictly the feed forward loop alone would be sufficient to achieve constant secondary speed so constituting an open loop control. For higher accuracy it is always desired to introduce a feedback loop consisting of a secondary shaft tachometer, which acts also on the transmission ratio. For very high performance, the feedback loop can be made to act slowly, whilst the feedforward loop corrects rapid variations of engine speed.

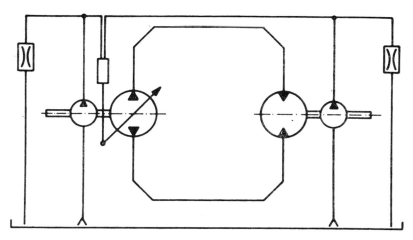

6.4–1 Circuit of constant speed drive using vane pumps and restrictors as tachometers on primary and secondary shafts

As indicated in the diagram, the leakage reduces flow by a constant amount, which is independent of the other operating variables, because secondary speed and system pressure are kept constant by the automatic control arrangement.

Instead of the tachometer on the secondary shaft, it is possible in some cases to use the system pressure developed by the secondary, itself as secondary speed indication. To implement this on the circuit

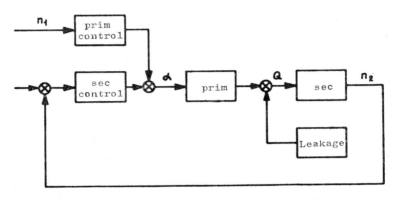

6.4-2 Functional diagram of constant speed drive with feedforward and feedback loop

in fig. 6.4–1, it is only necessary to remove the vane pump and restrictor on the secondary shaft and to introduce instead the system pressure in the primary actuator. Naturally this is possible only when the load torque is increasing continuously with secondary speed, and not subject to disturbing influences, in order to give an acceptable indication of secondary speed. This may be the case with some types of refrigeration compressors.

A constant speed hydrostatic drive does not need to reverse and the total speed range will not exceed 4:1. The lower ratios, especially, produced in a normal hydrostatic transmission at constant torque, are not needed here. With this restricted speed range, split power drives are of special advantage. Indeed all practical constant speed hydrostatic drives use some kind of split power as discussed in sections 4.2 and 4.3. For this application, being the inverse of a normal transmission, the inverse power split, with the secondary on the output shaft and primary on one branch shaft of a differential is preferable.

For constant speed alternator drives for aircraft a design using two differentials together with a variable hydrostatic transmission has become known. (Ref. 1).

EPILOGUE

In the foregoing the properties, advantages and limitations of hydrostatic transmissions have been discussed, together with the problems that arise with practical application.

It is the belief of the author that the use of hydrostatic transmission will increase considerably in the future. This will be only in part due to better hydrostatic units becoming available. Largely it will come as a consequence of the designers of the driven machines, specialists in their own fields, becoming familiar with the control and other properties of hydrostatic transmissions and the wonderful automatic machinery that can be built around them.

If this book does contribute a little towards this goal, it has fulfilled the hopes the author places in it.

Ref. 1: R. Westbury et. al. Hydrostatic alternator drive 1961 Conference of Oil hydraulic transmission and controls, The Institution of Mechanical Engineers, London.

APPENDIX A1

Additions to the mathematical formulation of losses

In this appendix the correct formulation of the torque losses, introduced in section 1.2a for positive operating variables, will be given for the case of positive or negative operating variables.

There are several possible sign conventions, but in this book, for normal pumping units, speed, displacement, flow and pressure are taken as positive, and only the torque as negative because it is opposed to the speed. Then the mechanical power, proportional to the product of torque and speed is negative, since power is entering the unit. The hydraulic power is proportional to the product of flow and pressure is positive, because power is leaving the unit. As explained in section 1.2–b, all operating variables can reverse sign, corresponding to the unit motoring, pumping in reverse, etc.

The leakage was formulated correctly for negative operating variables in section 1.2. The correct formulation of the various torque losses derives from the observation, that they are always opposed to shaft speed independently of the sense of pressure or displacement.

The correct formulation is thus:

$$M_f = -\frac{C_f}{2\pi} \frac{n}{|n|} |p| \, q_o \qquad \text{..} \qquad (A.1\text{--}1)$$

$$M_v = -\frac{C_v}{2\pi} n \mu q_o \qquad \text{..} \qquad (A.1\text{--}2)$$

$$M_h = \frac{C_h}{2\pi} \frac{n^3}{|n|} \frac{\alpha^4}{|\alpha|} I \qquad \text{..} \qquad (A.1\text{--}3)$$

These torque losses are negative because they are opposed to the positive shaft speed of the pumping unit. They are additive to the negative torque of an ideal pumping unit as shown by equation (1.2–9).

The consideration of negative operation variables is only necessary for the examination of reversing and braking drives. In many normal hydrostatic installations, where driving in one direction is predominant, as a simplification, all variables all taken as positive and extraordinary conditions like braking and reversing are considered separately.

APPENDIX A2

Structural and functional diagrams in engineering

a) *General properties and relations to other representations*

The description and analysis of the comparatively complex inter-actions between torque, speed, flow and pressure and the other operating variables of a hydrostatic drive in this book are based on extensive use of structural and functional diagrams. They afford a simple graphical representation of quantitative relations, and in this appendix its principal properties will be discussed.

A structural diagram is a representation of the elements of the structure of the installation, that can be more or less detailed or schematic. In hydraulics, structural diagrams range from schematic drawings and sketches to hydraulic circuits where components like pumps and valves are represented by conventional graphic symbols. In electronics they include very simple block circuits and the gener-ally used electronic circuits, where elements like transistors, resistors and capacitors are shown by suitable symbols. For a structural dia-gram it is essential that each element of the diagram corresponds to one or more actual components, and that each connection of the diagram corresponds to an actual connection, such as a fluid pipe, shaft or electric wire. Structural diagrams are most useful in hydraul-ic or electronic circuits to illustrate the functioning of the installa-tion without giving detailed information about components. like pumps, valves and transistors.

A functional diagram is a representation of the function of the components or group of components of an installation. Each ele-ment of the functional diagram corresponds to a function of a com-ponent. If one component has several functions it can be represented by several elements on the functional diagram. This method has been used for a long time in control engineering in block schemes and in this book functional diagrams are presented in the form of these. The connections between the blocks represent influences or signals between the components.

It should be mentioned that it is possible to draw different struct-ural and functional diagrams for each installation, depending on the detail desired and on which part or property of the installation is under examination.

The signal flow graphs in some textbooks on control engineering are functional diagrams exactly equivalent to block schemes but differing only by simplified graphical details. For practical engineering the author prefers functional diagrams with blocks in which can be written its function or the mathematical relationship between input and output.

b) *Details of functional diagrams*

A functional diagram as used in this book is a graphical representation of the interrelations of the different operating variables like speed, flow, pressure etc. Thus the interrelation takes place through the blocks each of which represents a function of the components of the installation. An operating variable exists in each connection and is designated by an appropriate letter ($nQ\rho$) written near to it.

Each block shows the causal and quantitative relation between the entering and leaving operating variables, or signals as they are sometimes called. The value of the leaving signal may depend on the rate of change or derivative of the entering signal, as for instance, the torque of a load with inertia depends on the derivative of the speed. Furthermore the leaving signal may depend on the integral of the entering signal, e.g. the pressure in a hydraulic accumulator is proportional to the integral of entering flow.

It is important that all blocks in functional diagrams are of unilateral action, that is, the leaving signal follows the signal entering and is not influenced by what happens to it further along the diagram. Disturbing influences, e.g. speed fluctuations of the pumping hydrostatic unit, are represented by special arrows entering the appropriate block from the side.

The signals entering and leaving a block may be of quite different physical nature or physical dimension, e.g. displacement setting and flow. Contrarily, the signals entering the addition and subtraction points must be of the same physical dimensions and the signals leaving such points have necessarily the same physical dimension. The same is true for signals leaving the branch points.

As a general remark, the correct use of physical dimensions on functional diagrams is a valuable help in gaining understanding of the process and avoiding errors. Such correct use is well developed in fluid mechanics in connection with model theory and in electrical engineering, but is unfortunately, a little neglected in some textbooks on control engineering.

The value of each operating variable is either entered as an input into the functional diagram, e.g. the displacement setting in most examples of hydrostatic transmission, or it originates from a block, as in fig. 3.3–1 when the flow from the block represents the pumping action of the primary. One of the operating variables may have useful effects outside the functional diagram, the secondary speed of a transmission, for example, and is normally called the output. It is important that the operating variable in a functional diagram always travels through the connection in a certain sense, as indicated by the arrow, and never in reverse, so representing a cause and effect relationship. In fig. 3.3–1 the flow is the effect of the pumping action and at the same time the cause of the secondary speed as shown by the arrow entering the second block. The secondary speed has no direct influence on the flow since the blocks represent unilateral relationship between cause (flow) and effect (secondary speed). Naturally, secondary speed causes opposing torque and pressure, which has some effect on the flow through leakage, as indicated by the feedback connection entering the first block in fig. 3.3–1 from below as disturbing influence. As an alternative it is possible to determine a leakage flow, as is done in fig. 3.3–2, which must be deducted from the ideal flow to give the flow effective for secondary speed.

Compared to structural diagrams the difference is that, in the functional diagram any action in reverse is represented by a special feedback connection, while in the structural diagram the reverse action becomes effective through the same connection. As an example, in a structural diagram the pressure responsible for diminution of effective flow acts backwards from secondary to primary through the main conduit. Only as long as the reverse or feedback action is negligibly small, can both diagrams be identical. In electronics this corresponds to a controlled voltage source feeding an electric load. If the current taken by the load has any influence on the voltage, this must be represented in a functional diagram by a special feedback connection, while it is taken into account in structural diagrams including electronic circuits by the internal resistance of the voltage source. As an example the reader is referred to page 101 of Bower (Bibliography, Ref. 2) for an elegant derivation of the functional diagram (block scheme) from a very simple electronic amplifier circuit.

The functional diagram furthermore has branch points where the signal branches into two or more connections as in fig. 3.3–3, in which the pressure affects both leakage and primary torque. Since the configuration downstream (that is in the direction of the arrow) has no influence on the value of the particular variable, it is the same everywhere and independent of the number of branches. This is also different to a structural diagram, where the branching of a line divides a flow or where in the case of electrical branch points the Kirchhoff laws on currents are applicable. Finally there are addition and subtraction points, represented by a circle with a cross, where the signal in the outgoing connection is the sum or difference of the entering connections as indicated by appropriate plus or minus signs.

Since in a functional diagram each block represents a function of a component there can be two or more blocks related to one component. As an example, in fig. 3.3–2, the relationships between effective flow and secondary speed and between secondary torque and pressure, each represented by one block, take place within the secondary hydrostatic unit. For identification it is usual to write in the blocks the functions either by words as in fig. 3.1–1, or by mathematical symbols representing the entering and leaving signals. In the example fig. 3.3–2, the second block in the upper row and the last right hand block of the lower row are equivalent to the equations:

$$n_2 = \frac{Q_e}{q_0} \quad \text{and} \quad p = \frac{2\pi M_2}{q_0} \qquad \qquad .. \quad (A.2\text{–}1)$$

Furthermore there are several possible choices as to which operating variables should be the cause and which the effect. For example in fig. 2.1–2 the transmission produces secondary speed which is the cause of the opposing torque, the influence of which on the secondary speed is represented by the feedback connection entering the block for the production of secondary speed. Conversely in fig. 2.2–2 the transmission produces torque with consequent rotation of the load, and the speed has an influence on the torque of the transmission. Which representation is preferable depends on the individual case and on the magnitude of the influencing forces.

In some functional diagrams Fu blocks or functional boxes are used, which show a functional relationship between input and output. This may take any form, but in some cases it is brought about simply by a member with play or with a dead zone engaging after the input has reached a certain value. One example is a relief valve, where the spool begins to move only after the pressure has reached the calibrated value.

Important information is the maximum allowable value of each operating variable. It can be included in the functional diagram by writing the allowable values near each connection. These maximum values (e.g. maximum torque and speed) determine directly the size and cost of the corresponding physical installation.

c) *Use of functional diagrams*

With the above conventions a functional diagram is a powerful method of representing the interaction of causes and effects for a variety of physical structures including hydraulic installations. Unpredictable causes, like external torque fluctuations in hydrostatic drives and stray voltage pick ups in electronics can be represented as disturbing influences by arrows entering an appropriate block.

The representation afforded by a functional diagram is perfectly general, and it has not been postulated that the functional diagram should be linear, and in fact some functional diagrams in this book are essentially nonlinear.

Functional diagrams can be programmed directly on analogue computers, where it is usual to represent highly nonlinear parts such as functional boxes by biased diodes. The programming consists of building an electrical analogue to all operating variables by using suitable scale factors (see Rogers Bibliography, ref. 15 and sec. 1.0–3). By changing the input and entering disturbances on the computer, the behaviour of the operating variables can be quickly explored. The establishment of a representative functional diagram is always a necessary preliminary to the calculations from which the computer can be programmed.

In many cases functional diagrams can be considered linear in sufficient approximation. Then the whole highly developed body of linear control theory (Gille Bibliography, ref. 6) can be brought to bear on the problem, and in particular the Laplace transformation and the different stability and performance criteria. (see Bower Bibliography, ref. 2).

In linear systems the output is proportional to the input. The ratio of output to input is called the transfer function. It is independent of the input amplitude but may be frequency dependent.

The power of analysis and synthesis of the linear method is such that it is applied often to functional diagrams, where a linear approximation does not seem justified on the physical grounds.

If the system is not linear, it can very often be considered linear for a restricted range of values of the operating variables and the linear method applied. This amounts to replacing curved characteristics by straight segments and is used frequently, for the curved characteristics of servo valves (ref. Lewis Bibliography, ref. 13) and transistors. This method is known as the "small signal" theory, and is very suitable for the investigation of stability for certain values of the operating variables.

Finally there are functional diagrams with essentially non-linear components such as on-off controllers e.g. electric switches or hydraulic two-position valves, which are not amenable to small signal analysis. Here it is often possible to make a Fourier expansion of the output of the non linear element and to neglect the higher harmonics. This is called the describing function analysis of non-linear control theory (Gille Bibliography, ref. 6).

In practical engineering it is in the experience of the author, always desirable to establish a functional diagram, which is a very vivid representation of the installation and then to base the further reasoning upon it. It helps as an aid to intuition, and shows which influences are important and which may be neglected. In hydrostatic transmission applications it is normally not necessary to go into the above refined mathematical analysis referred to above.

Special rules of manipulation[1] exist for obtaining from a functional diagram, established by physical reasoning, simpler functional diagrams and finally the transfer function relationship of input and output. They are very suitable for obtaining quantitative relationships in hydraulic components and hydrostatic transmission.

---

[1]Rules of manipulation are summarized by Gosling (Bibliography Ref. 8). See also G. J. Thaler, Nonlinear feedback control systems Section 4–2 and fig. 4–12, Mc Graw Hill, 1962.

BIBLIOGRAPHY

THIS bibliography is by no means exhaustive, it simply cites a few titles the author has found useful for work on hydrostatic transmission.

1) J. F. BLACKBURN, Fluid Power Control, Wiley 1960 "written by many authors reflecting thinking and practice of the group at M.I.T. (USA) developing hydraulic missile controls."

2) J. L. BOWER et al. Design of Servomechanics, Wiley 1958 "Introductionary text, showing practical design and performance aspects, with hydraulic examples."

3) A. DURR & O. WACHTER, Hydraulische Antriebe Carl Hanser Muenchen 1954 (in German). "Gives an introduction, illustrated by many designs to hydraulics and machine tool feeds and controls."

4) W. ERNST, Oil hydraulic power, 2nd edition McGraw Hill 1960 "Comprehensive book on all aspects of hydraulic equipment in industry, illustrating American practice".

5) D. D. FULLER, Lubrication, Wiley 1956 (also in German) "Engineering textbook on hydrodynamical and hydrostatic lubrication covering theory and practice".

6) J. C. GILLE et al. Feedback control systems, McGraw Hill 1960. Also in French (original) German, Russian, Polish. Comprehensive "Textbook from beginning to control components with chapters on mechanical components and hydraulic servo-systems".

7) M. GUILLON Systèmes hydrauliques Dunod 1961 (in French) "Theory and practice of feedback hydraulic and electro-hydraulic systems including servovalves, written by a known aircraft control designer and teacher.

8) W. GOSLING, Engineering Systems, Heywood 1962 "easily read introduction to systems engineering emphasising functional and structural diagrams from the point of view of telecommunications, useful for hydraulic and mechanical systems".

9) R. HADECKEL, Displacement pumps and motors, Pitman 1950 "Comprehensive theoretical treatment of the geometry of all possible forms of hydraulic units, including some very unusual ones".

10) J. C. HUNSACKER & B. G. RIGHTMIRE, Engineering Fluid mechanics 1947 "Clear treatment of fluid mechanics for engineering with emphasis on dimensional analysis, including chapters on hydrostatic transmissions and bearing theory".

11) G. HUTAREW, Regelungstechnik (in German) Springer 1961 "Elements of automatic control theory and components, from the point of view of turbine governing, but useful for any mechanical feedback control problem".

12) H. KRUG Flüssigkeitsgetriebe bei Werkzeugmaschinen Springer 1959 (in German). "Comprehensive treatment of hydraulics and hydraulic drives from the point of view of machine tool designer".

13) E. LEWIS & H. STERN, Hydraulic Control Systems, McGraw Hill 1962. Book with emphasis on dynamic behaviour of hydraulic controls, using extensively functional diagrams.

14) A. C. MORSE, Electrohydraulic Servomechanisms, McGraw Hill 1963 "Book written for the quantitative design of servo-systems, with treatment of component design".

15) A. E. ROGERS, Analogue Computation in Engineering McGraw Hill 1960 "Emphasises the practical aspects of solving a given problem on analogue computor, with reference to design use".

16) WARREN E. WILSON, Positive Displacement pumps and motors Pitman 1950 "Description and classic theoretical treatment of hydrostatic unit with hints on laboratory experiments".

INDEX